Group Crisis Intervention

Student Manual

5th Edition
revised

Jeffrey T. Mitchell, Ph.D., CCISM

Co-Founder

International Critical Incident Stress Foundation (ICISF)

Clinical Professor of Emergency Health Services

University of Maryland Baltimore County

Critical Incident Stress Management (CISM): Group Crisis Intervention, 5th Edition (revised) by Jeffrey T. Mitchell, PH.D.,

Books may be purchased by contacting the publisher at:
International Critical Incident Stress Foundation, Inc.
3290 Pine Orchard Lane, Suite 106
Ellicott City, MD 21042
(410) 750-9600
(410) 750-9601 fax
www.icisf.org

Note: The author may be contacted at the same address.

Cover Design: Christina Lippincott
Publisher: International Critical Incident Stress Foundation, Inc.
Editor: Judith Reveal
1) Critical Incident Stress Management, 2) Critical Incident Stress Debriefing, 3) Group Crisis Intervention, 4) Resiliency
Fifth Edition (revised)
Printed in the United States of America
Print ISBN# 978-0-9795692-8-9
E-version ISBN# 978-0-9795692-0-3

Table of Contents

About the Author

Jeffrey T. Mitchell, Ph.D, CTS, CCISM is a Clinical Professor and a Graduate Faculty member of the Emergency Health Services Department at the University of Maryland in Baltimore County Maryland, (UMBC) and President Emeritus of the International Critical Incident Stress Foundation. He began his teaching experience as an elementary and middle school science teacher. He earned his Ph.D. in Human Development from the University of Maryland. After serving as a firefighter/paramedic he developed a comprehensive, integrated, systematic, and multi-component crisis intervention program called "Critical Incident Stress Management." He has authored more than 275 articles and 19 books in the stress and crisis intervention fields. He serves as an adjunct faculty member of the Emergency Management Institute of the Federal Emergency Management Agency. He is a reviewer for the *Journal of the American Medical Association*, the *American Journal of Disaster Medicine*, and the *International Journal of Emergency Mental Health and Resiliency*. The Austrian Red Cross honored him with the Bronze Medal for his Crisis Intervention work during the Kaprun railway tunnel fire in 2000.

Dr. Mitchell achieved board certification in traumatic stress and credentialing as a Diplomat and a Member of the Board of Scientific and Professional Advisors of the American Academy of Experts in Traumatic Stress. The Association of Traumatic Stress Specialists has approved him as a Certified Trauma Specialist. The United Nations appointed him to the United Nations Department of Safety and Security Working Group on Stress. In 2007, The United Nations formed a Critical Incident Stress Management Unit that currently serves UN employees worldwide.

Dr. Jeffrey T. Mitchell originated the multi-component field of Critical Incident Stress Management (CISM) and personally developed key components of the field such as individual support services and the interactive group processes of defusing and Critical Incident Stress Debriefing (CISD).

Important Supporting Resources

Everly, G. S., Jr., & Mitchell, J. T. (2008). *Integrative crisis intervention and disaster mental health.* Ellicott City, MD: Chevron Publishing Corporation.

Everly, G. S., Jr., & Mitchell, J. T. (2013). *CISM: Key papers and core concepts in crisis intervention and human resilience.* Ellicott City, MD: Chevron Publishing.

Mitchell, J. T. (2004). Characteristics of successful early intervention programs. *International Journal of Emergency Mental Health, 6*(4), 175-184.

Mitchell, J. T. (2007). *Group crisis support: Why it works, when and how to provide it.* Ellicott City, MD: Chevron Publishing.

Mitchell, J. T. (2011). Collateral damage in disaster workers. *International Journal of Emergency Mental Health, 13*(2), 121-125.

Mitchell, J. T. (2011). Critical decision points in crisis support: Using checklists and flowcharts in psychological crises. *International Journal of Emergency Mental Health, 13*(3), 137-146.

Mitchell, J. T. (2012). Memorial architecture: Less we forget. In Charles Figley (Ed), *International Encyclopedia of Trauma.* New York: Sage Publications.

Mitchell, J. T. (2012). Critical incident stress. In Charles Figley (Ed), *International Encyclopedia of Trauma.* New York: Sage Publications.

Mitchell, J. T. (2013). *Care and feeding of a successful critical incident management team.* Ellicott City, MD: Chevron Publishing.

Author's Note: Essential information to read before starting the course.

The contents of this student manual are provided as a set of general guidelines only. Neither the Group Crisis Intervention course nor this Group Crisis Intervention Student Manual are intended to be used as a self-help program or as a substitute for psychotherapy or professional mental health guidance. When in doubt about one's mental health, always consult a licensed mental health professional. Similarly, this manual may not be used as a substitute for formal Critical Incident Stress Management (CISM) training, supervision, or field experience. The guidelines in this student manual should be used only by those who are properly trained and qualified to do so.

The content of this Group Crisis Intervention course may be emotionally distressing to some participants. Participants are encouraged to leave the training at any point should they find the material excessively distressing. The instructor will be available to participants during the training to discuss any adverse reactions to the course material, should this occur.

Please understand that when individuals have experienced past traumatic events, current events or circumstances and even classroom presentations can remind people of past situations and uncomfortable or even painful memories can be brought to mind. This is _not_ abnormal, but it can be distressing. In severe cases, considerable psychological distress and even physical manifestations of the distress can be stimulated. In most cases the painful memories and physical symptoms will recede and the person will recover from the distress fairly quickly. If the distress continues unabated, it would be wise for the distressed person to seek psychotherapy to help reduce one's sensitivity to the past traumatic memories.

It is best to resolve one's own upsetting memories and physical symptoms before working with people in a current state of crisis. It is potentially harmful to people dealing with a current crisis to suddenly experience significant distress in the person who is supposed to be helping them.

4

Core Elements of CISM

Note: Material in this manual is organized into *three* main categories:

** IMPORTANT INFORMATION **

Must-know information to understand CISM concepts

*** CRITICAL INFORMATION ***

Essential guidelines used in direct CISM applications

* ADDITIONAL INFORMATION *

Interesting or worth some attention

** IMPORTANT INFORMATION **

Understanding the Core Elements of CISM

Six core elements of CISM have repeatedly been identified during the last forty plus years of CISM services. They are:

1. Assessment and Triage of people in crisis
2. Listening skills, The SAFER-R model, and individual crisis intervention.
3. Informational group processes.
4. Interactive group processes.
5. Strategic Planning, Incident Assessment, Operations Management, Theme, Target, Types, Timing, and Team
6. Personal and Community Resilience. (*Resiliency includes the concepts of resistance, resilience, and recovery.*)

The six core elements are extremely important. They guide the overall field of Critical Incident Stress Management (CISM). Critical Incident Stress Management is a program or package of many crisis intervention techniques that are combined and blended to provide the most effective support for distressed people. The six core elements influence the order of presentation of courses and the order of presentation within courses. They also influence the application of the crisis intervention techniques in real crisis situations. In this student manual, specific Core Elements of CISM will be identified in each section.

Course Objectives

At the conclusion of this course the participants will be able to:

1. Define key crisis intervention terms such as "critical incident," "crisis," and "crisis intervention." (see pgs. 16-18)
2. Define key stress management terms such as "stress," "traumatic stress," and "Critical Incident Stress Management (CISM)." (see pgs. 25-27)
3. Explain the role of the comprehensive, integrated, systematic, and multi-component crisis intervention system known as "Critical Incident Stress Management (CISM)." (see pgs. 25-27)
4. Understand the nature of "resistance," "resiliency," and "recovery" in the field of CISM. (see pg. 16 and pgs. 136-140)
5. List the components of a CISM program. (see pgs. 49-54)
6. Briefly describe the five elements of CISM's strategic planning formula. (see pgs. 47-49)
7. Explain the differences between Informational and Interactive group crisis intervention procedures. (In *Informational* groups, concepts, guidelines, instructions and information are shared in a structured manner. In *Interactive* groups, there is an active discussion between group members and the CISM team.)
8. Practice, by participation in role-play scenarios, the Informational Group Crisis Interventions such as a) Rest, Information and Transition Services (RITS) and b) Crisis Management Briefing (CMB).
9. Practice, by participation in role-play scenarios, the Interactive Group Crisis Interventions such as a) Defusing and b) Critical Incident Stress Debriefing (CISD).
10. Explain the potential risks of adverse outcomes if the standards of CISM practice are violated or if untrained people attempt to conduct group crisis intervention sessions.

NOTE: All the terms in the list of objectives will be explained in the sections to follow. This list of objective simply identifies a broad overview of what is covered in the book. Do not get stuck on this list now, but wait to the material is explained in the actual course material.

Course Topical Outline

Note: Expect variation in the course presentations. The topical outline to follow does not restrict an instructor. It simply provides an overview of the content of the course for the students. Instructors have an instructor's manual that provides them with specific guidelines about what must be covered in the Group Crisis Intervention Course. It also provides instructors with guidelines regarding timing of the various topics.

Instructor style, the option of instructors to use certain audio-visuals to enhance the presentation of material, specific group needs and questions from the participants may impact the exact timing of the presentation of this course. There may also be alterations in the order in which certain material is presented. Outside of the _Important_ and _Critical_ information, some segments of the material in this student manual may be assigned to students to read on their own and will not, therefore, be covered during class time. The information in this course, however, should generally comply with the topics outlined below. I hope the course is helpful to you and to those you serve. Thank you for your interest in Crisis Intervention and Critical Incident Stress Management.

Jeffrey T. Mitchell, Ph.D., CCISM

Group Crisis Intervention
(Topical Outline Only. This outline does not require adherence to specific times or to a specific order of presentation. It simply informs the students of the topics typically covered in the Group Crisis Intervention course.)

Day 1

Introduction

A)   Registration, student manual distribution, and introductions
B)   Welcome and introductory remarks
    1) Instructor introduction
    2) Course overview
    3) Course ground rules and guidelines
    4) Special circumstances and cautions
    5) Identification of professions present
    6) ICISF – its background, roles and services
    7) Answer any recourse questions

Section One – Crisis Intervention and Critical Incident Stress Management
Key Terms and Concepts

A)   Background
B)   Resiliency Model in Crisis Intervention Work and Stress Management
C)   Key Terms and Concepts: Crisis and Crisis Intervention
    1) Critical Incidents
    2) Crisis
    3) Critical Incident Stress
    4) Types of Crises
    5) Characteristics of Crises
    6) Crisis Intervention
D)   A brief History of Crisis Intervention
    1) Brief historical overview of crisis intervention
    2) Milestones in Crisis Intervention
E)   Application Essentials
    1) Providers of Crisis Intervention
    2) Goals of Crisis Intervention
    3) Principles of Crisis Intervention

F) Steps in Crisis Intervention
  1) Introduction
  2) Assess situation and impact on the people involved
  3) Mentally list all possible options
  4) Choose best option
  5) Implement the best option immediately
  6) Reassess
  7) Maintain, change, or abandon the option
  8) Closure of intervention
I) Critical incident stress management (CISM)
  1) Critical Incident Stress Debriefing (CISD)
  2) CISM in its proper context
J) Core components of CISM
  1) Assessment and Triage
  2) Individual Crisis Intervention
  3) Informational group processes
  4) Interactive group processes
  5) Strategic planning and operations management
  6) Personal and community resilience

Section Two - Stress
Psychological and Behavioral Reactions To Stressors

A) Human stress: basic terms and conditions
  1) Stressor
  2) Stress or Stress Response
  3) Target Organs
B) Types of stress
  1) Burnout
  2) Cumulative stress
    a) Stress Arousal
    b) Energy Conservation Phase
    c) Exhaustion Phase
  3) Eustress
  4) Distress
C) Traumatic Stress
  1) Trauma
  2) Traumatic Stress
  3) Post Traumatic Stress
  4) Post-Traumatic Stress Disorder (PTSD)
  5) Criteria for Post-Traumatic Stress Disorder
  6) Psycho-traumatology
  7) Trauma Membrane
D) Early Psychological Intervention
  1) National Institutes of Mental Health report
E) Symptoms of Distress

10

1) Cognitive
2) Emotional
3) Behavioral
4) Physical
5) Spiritual

Section Three – Strategic Planning in Crisis Intervention and Critical Incident Stress Management

A)   Staff Support Programs
B)   Strategic Crisis Support Programs
C)   The "Five T" Formula for Developing a crisis strategy
    1) Theme(s) / Threats
    2) Target(s)
    3) Types
    4) Timing of the interventions
    5) Team(s) (who provides the assistance)
D)   Tactical Components of Critical Incident Stress Management (CISM)
E)   Critical Incident Stress Debriefing (CISD)
    1) Commonly Used Crisis Intervention Tactics (Table)

Section Four – Informational Group Crisis Interventions

A)   Rest, Information, and Transition Services (RITS)
    1) Definition
    2) Time
    3) Application
    4) Target
    5) Providers
    6) Location
    7) Goals
    8) Process
    9) Contraindications
    10) Components
    11) Presentation Points
    12) Key Concepts

B)   Crisis Management Briefing (CMB)
    1) Definition
    2) Application
    3) Time
    4) Goals
    5) Providers
    6) Process

7) Frequency
8) Follow-up

Day Two

Section Five – Interactive Group Crisis Intervention: Defusing

A)   Introduction and Background
B)   Principles of Group Support
    1) Heterogeneous groups
    2) Homogeneous groups
    3) Types of groups
    4) Healing Factors in groups
C)   Defusing
    1) Definition
    2) Description
    3) Uses
    4) Contraindications
    5) Three components or stages
      a) Introduction
      b) Exploration
      c) Information
      d) Notes on defusing

Section Six – Practice Exercises for Defusing

A)   Exercise One: Introductory Remarks for Defusing
B)   Exercise Two: Defusing Practice
C)   Observing a Defusing

Section Seven - Interactive Group Crisis Intervention: Critical Incident Stress Debriefing (CISD)

A)   Critical Incident Stress Debriefing (CISD)
    1) Definition
    2) Overview
    3) Description
    4) Structure
    5) Homogenous Groups and CISD
    6) Goals of CISD
    7) Applications and uses
    8) Benefits of CISD

Section Eight – Interactive Groups Process - CISD
CISD role-play practice session

Intervention	Type	Activity	Target	Timing	Duration	Trigger
RITS – Rest Information Transition Services	Information + Rest + Food	Passive	Staff Only. **NOT** general public	After shift	10 min. info 20 mins. food / rest	Large scale or major event
CMB Crisis Management Briefing	Information only even when questions are asked	Passive Sometimes with Q/A Sometimes without Q/A	Any large group Works well even when group is hetero-geneous	Before, during, after event. May be used many times if info is new each time	20 to 30 minutes is ideal	Any event with impact on large group
Defusing	Interactive Group. Members may help others in group	Active	Close knit group **Only. homo-gene-ous**	Up to 8 hours after event	20 – 45 minutes max	Event impact on close knit group
CISD Critical Incident Stress Debriefing	Interactive Group with 7 specific stages. Group members may help others in group	Very active	Close knit group **Only. Homo-gene-ous**	24 -72 hours post event is ideal	1 to 3 hrs.	Event impact on close knit group

Section One
Key Terms and Concepts:
Crisis and Crisis Intervention

Something to think about:
"We presume that we would be ready for battle if confronted with a great crisis, but it is not the crisis that builds something within us – it simply reveals what we are made of already."
– Oswald Chambers, Clergyman, British Army Chaplain, WWI

<u>Note</u>: *The primary principles of crisis intervention apply to the assistance applied to both individuals and to groups involved in a crisis. Although the focus in this particular course is on group crisis intervention processes, some of the material in this section may have previously been covered in the Assisting Individuals in Crisis Course. We apologize for any repetition. The intention, in this section, is not to repeat, but to assure that the crisis intervention material is clear and complete.*

The core elements of CISM covered in this section are in bold and enlarged letters below:

1. **Assessment and Triage of people in crisis**
2. **Listening skills, The SAFER-R model, and individual crisis intervention.**
3. Informational group processes.
4. Interactive group processes.
5. Strategic Planning, Incident assessment, Operations management, Theme, *Target, Types, Timing, and Team*
6. **Personal and Community resilience. (Resiliency includes the concepts of *resistance, resilience, and recovery)***

Introduction and Background

Instructors from countries other than the United States will frequently provide statistics and studies that more clearly represent the state of crisis intervention in those lands.

In 1999, the US Surgeon General's Report on Mental Illness noted that 80% of Americans will be exposed to a traumatic event (critical incident) in the course of their lives and about 10% of those exposed will develop negative psychological consequences. The rate of exposure for military and emergency services personnel is even higher and, regardless of their training and experience, they are not exempt from negative psychological outcomes.

The majority of people exposed to traumatic events experience a heightened emotional state called a *crisis*. Some crises can generate extreme levels of emotional turmoil. Experience indicates that most people benefit from immediate and carefully presented support services while they are struggling through the crisis reaction, especially if the reaction is severe. Crisis reactions can be mitigated and restoration to adaptive function can be achieved if appropriately trained crisis interventionists utilize a set of standardized crisis intervention principles and procedures.

The principles and practices of crisis intervention are not only helpful for individuals, but they may also be applied to heterogeneous groups and homogeneous groups who have experienced a communal crisis. *It should be very clear, however, that different interventions are used for individuals than those that are used for groups. Different types of groups need different types of group interventions.* This student manual and the course for which it was developed will guide the participant through a training process that will enhance their overall crisis intervention skills and provide specific procedures that are applicable to distressed **groups** depending on the circumstances.

Crisis intervention is a flexible support process that adapts to the needs of people in a crisis state. Although it has therapeutic features and can be practiced by mental health professionals, it is not psychotherapy nor is it a substitute for psychotherapy.

For Understanding Crisis and CISM Concepts

The Resiliency Model in Crisis Intervention Work and Stress Management

From the very beginning, the field of Critical Incident Stress Management was, and continues to be, a crisis system based on a resiliency model. It aims at building resistance before exposure to traumatic events. It focuses on rebounding from stress. In those cases where people need additional care, the CISM program is uniquely positioned to assist individuals in finding appropriate professional care.

- **Resistance** - Resistance is the ability of individuals, groups, organizations and entire populations to resist distress, impairment and dysfunction.

- **Resilience** - The ability to rapidly rebound or recoil from distress, and to rise above adversity.

- **Recovery** - The resolution, repair, reconstruction, restoration, and rebuilding of the human spirit, mind, and body after sustaining the damages incurred by prolonged, extreme or overwhelming distress.

Key Terms and Concepts: Crisis and Crisis Intervention

- *Critical Incidents:*

  Critical Incidents are powerful, traumatic events that initiate the crisis response. Each profession can list its own most awful traumatic events. Below is a sample list from the emergency services professions. The list has been nicknamed the "terrible ten." These traumatic events may overwhelm the coping ability of individuals or groups exposed to the incident. They are among the worst situations that can arise in military and emergency services operations, but they are, by no means, the only traumatic events that can be encountered by those groups.

1. Suicide of a colleague
2. Line of duty death (work place death)
3. Serious line of duty injury
4. Disaster / multiple casualty incident
5. Police shooting / accidental killing or wounding of an innocent person
6. Significant events involving children
7. Prolonged incidents especially with a loss of life
8. Personally threatening situations
9. Events with excessive media interest
10. Any significant event capable of causing considerable emotional distress for those who are exposed to it.

- ***Crisis:***

  An acute emotional, cognitive and physical _reaction_ to a powerful, horrible, awful, terrifying, threatening, or grotesque stimulus or to an overwhelming demand or circumstance.

- ***Critical Incident Stress***

  A state of heightened cognitive, physical, emotional, and behavioral arousal that accompanies the crisis (a crisis is sometimes referred to as the _crisis reaction_.) Experiencing a critical incident triggers this elevated state of arousal. If a person or a group does not manage Critical Incident Stress and resolve it appropriately, it may lead to one or more significant problems such as physical illnesses, insecurity, chronic anxiety, rage reactions, marital or relationship discord, abuse of alcohol and other substances, withdrawal from others or even psychological disorders including Acute Stress Disorder, panic attacks or panic disorder, depression, and Posttraumatic Stress Disorder (PTSD).

- *Types of Crises:*

  1. Maturational (Associated with changes in various stages of life, for example, being a teenager, adulthood, midlife, aging, or retirement)
  2. Situational (Associated with events like accidents, deaths, disaster, violence, property losses, illness, or threats)

- *Characteristics of Crises:*

  1. Disruption to one's general state of psychological balance
  2. Usual coping mechanisms fail
  3. Distress, impairment, or dysfunction.

- *Crisis Intervention:*

  Crisis intervention is a **temporary, active, and supportive** entry into the life situation of an individual or of a group during a period of extreme distress. *Different intervention procedures are used for individuals than those that are used for groups. This course focuses on the **group** crisis intervention techniques.*

* ADDITIONAL INFORMATION *

A Brief History of Crisis Intervention:

Some aspects of this Crisis Intervention history may be provided as part of the instructor's presentation. Most instructors summarized some key points and assign this segment as an out-of-class reading assignment.

Knowing the history of the field of crisis intervention helps us to understand better the objectives and methods of crisis intervention that have been developed over time. Crisis intervention was first applied and documented by the French army during the Franco – Prussian War in 1870-71. They employed simple procedures such as removing distressed soldiers from the front lines, in other words, reducing war stimuli. They also provided nutritious meals, rest, and an opportunity to talk to medical personnel. They were able to calm distressed soldiers and restore the majority of them to function on the battlefield. Those basic approaches to crisis intervention still have value today.

In 1906, Eduard Stierlin, a Swiss psychiatrist, provided psychological support to the victims and family members of miners after a great mining disaster killed 1100 miners in northern France near the border with Germany.

In World War I, The Americans, under the leadership of psychiatrist, Dr. Thomas Salmon, followed the French example and cared for American soldiers with psychological support services provided immediately behind the front lines. About 65% returned to combat in 3 or 4 days. Without crisis support only 40% returned to combat and it took 3 to 4 weeks.

Since the World War II, Crisis intervention has also been known as "psychological first aid," "Emotional first aid," and "early psychological intervention." The same history, theory base, and core principles apply regardless of name of the support program.

The use of the term, "Psychological First Aid" can be traced to before World War II. (Dewey, 1933) It appeared in civilian and military circles and meant a variety of support services. One WWII London rescuer, later wrote, "Every night, from dusk to dawn, the German bombs fell upon them. Woolton suggested that I might go down about six o'clock when the 'all clear' sounded and see what I could do to help. I found that, as they came out of the shelters, what comforted them was a kiss and a cup of tea." (Robert Boothby, 1978).

Other authors describe Psychological First Aid as a _debriefing tool_ for soldiers or for the US Merchant Marine. (Blain, Hoch, & Ryan, 1945). One prominent British author states that Psychological First Aid was employed as large group counseling sessions for soldiers following battle. (Terr, 1992).

In 1944, after the horrific Cocoanut Grove fire in Boston, Massachusetts, Erik Lindemann and Gerald Caplan established the principles and some core practices still used today.

By the mid 1950's, at the beginning of the "Cold War," Psychological First Aid was commonly applied in disasters. (American Psychiatric Association Committee on Civil Defense, 1954). In fact, at that time Psychological First Aid was seen as a very broad spectrum of support services to assist people in crisis. Consider, for a moment, the following quote from F.C. Thorn, editor of the *Journal of Clinical Psychology* in 1952:

"Prophylactically, [from the prevention point of view], it is probable that many disorders could be nipped in the bud if prompt attention could be given...First aid treatment by its very nature should be very flexible and expedient, utilizing every possible method of achieving results..."

By the 1960s Gerald Caplan had clearly demonstrated his knowledge and skill in crisis intervention and his writings stand out as benchmarks against which we can measure all other crisis intervention programs.

In the early 1970's, Jeffrey T. Mitchell of the University of Maryland Baltimore County began writing about the needs of emergency personnel for crisis support after traumatic events. He developed many of the crisis intervention procedures used around the world today. His work is the foundation of a broad-spectrum crisis intervention program known as Critical Incident Stress Management (CISM).

The International Critical Incident Stress Foundation (ICISF) was co-founded by Dr. George S. Everly, Jr. and Dr. Jeffrey T. Mitchell in 1989. It provides crisis intervention and stress management training to many thousands of people each year. ICISF is known for its support services to emergency personnel and many other populations. It has a network of over 1500 Critical Incident Stress Management teams that operate in about one hundred countries.

Crisis Intervention support services have been utilized in thousands of disasters and uncountable numbers of smaller tragedies. Theses supportive interventions have made a difference in the lives of literally hundreds of thousands of people. Crisis Intervention services continue to be developed, expanded, and refined under the leadership of the International Critical Incident Stress Foundation, as well through the efforts of numerous Federal, State and private entities.

*** CRITICAL INFORMATION ***

Application Essentials

- ### *Providers of Crisis Intervention:*

  Some mental health professionals provide certain crisis intervention services. Firefighters, emergency medical personnel, law enforcement personnel, doctors, nurses, search and rescue personnel, clergy personnel, hospital workers, communications personnel and community members are the most common providers of crisis intervention services.

  Dr. Gerald Caplan, in the early 1970's, said at large conference on crisis intervention in Baltimore, Maryland that "...*excellent help may be provided by friends, family and colleagues who do not have formal mental health training.*" It was his remarks that encouraged the development of peer support programs around the world.

  Crisis intervention services should always serve as a link to formal mental health services when such services are necessary.

- ### *Goals of Crisis Intervention:*

  1. Lower emotional tension, stabilize the person, mobilize a person's resources, and mitigate the impact of the traumatic event.

2. Normalize their reactions and facilitate normal recovery processes, in normal people who are experiencing normal reactions to abnormal events.
3. Restore individuals to adaptive functions and to enhance unit cohesion and unit performance in homogeneous groups.
4. Identification of individuals who may need professional care and to assure that those individuals receive appropriate referrals.

- *Principles of Crisis Intervention:*

   1. **Simplicity** – People respond to simple, not complex issues, during a crisis. Interventions should be simple.
   2. **Brevity** – short contacts from a few minutes up to a maximum of 1 hour. It is typical to have 3-5 contacts to complete crisis intervention work.
   3. **Innovation** – Crisis Intervention providers must be creative to manage unique and emotionally painful situations. Thinking of novel solutions is often necessary.
   4. **Pragmatism** – Suggestions must be practical if they are to work in resolving a crisis.
   5. **Proximity** – Most effective crisis intervention contacts occur closer to the operational zone or in someone's comfort zone. In crisis intervention, we still make "house calls."
   6. **Immediacy** – A crisis reaction demands rapid intervention. Delays cause more pain and complications.
   7. **Expectancy** – When possible the crisis intervener works to set up expectations of a reasonable positive outcome.

- **Steps in Crisis Intervention**
   (Adapted from the work of Dr. Albert Roberts, Crisis Intervention Handbook, Assessment, Treatment and Research, 2005.)

   1. **Introduction** of support person(s). People in a state of crisis are often emotionally overwhelmed and their cognitive functions sometimes are slowed and confused. It is extremely important that crisis workers and support personnel introduce themselves and explain briefly their role in the situation. This

is a time when the crisis interventionist begins assessing the impact of the situation on the individuals and groups involved. Be sure to obtain the names and relationships of the people you are attempting to assist. You can gain insights into the level of distress by how the people in crisis answer your questions.

2. **Assess situation and impact on the people involved.** Assessment should not only look at the incident itself. The incident or situation is certainly important. Crisis work, however, requires that you assess carefully the people involved. Some may be overwhelmed and expressing their distress quite openly. Others may be keeping their distress hidden inside themselves. Still others may not be as upset by a situation as we might have predicted. Keep in mind that trauma is in the eye of the beholder. If a person does not perceive something as disturbing, then, for that person, the event may not be distressing. Crisis intervention personnel should not be trying to make everyone react the same way. Some will be visibly distressed and in need of support. Others will not be seriously impacted by an event, even when everyone expects them to be distressed.

3. **Mentally list all possible options.** As you assess the nature and magnitude of the event and the impact on the people involved in the event you should begin to make a mental list of the possible options available to manage the crisis reactions. One or more of those mental options will probably be employed to reduce the distress and move the person toward crisis resolution. By making this mental list of options, you are beginning to develop a crisis action plan.

4. **Choose best option.** Start by asking the person or people involved in the situation if they know what might help them to deal with the situation. (You might not have thought of the options mentioned by those involved, but they may be very worthwhile options). If the person cannot focus on any crisis plan then you should draw from you mental list some potential actions that might help to reduce the crisis state. You should be able to focus on some suggestions that the person is willing

to try. Together you develop a ***crisis action plan*** and prepare to set that plan in motion.

5. **Implement the best option immediately**. Once you decide on the crisis action plan, you must get some action going immediately to prevent the person from sinking back into a state of mental confusion and extreme distress. Focusing on carrying out a plan helps the person to regain control and reduce anxiety.

6. **Reassess**. Once the plan is in action, the crisis interventionist should monitor the progress of the individual or group receiving assistance.

7. **Maintain, change, or abandon the option.** If the plan appears to be having positive effects (the person calms down and thinking becomes more clear, and he or she initiates helpful behaviors on their own), then it should be kept going. If the crisis action plan is not having positive effects or if the person is strongly resisting the plan, then the plan needs to be altered. If the plan worked well and the goals of the intervention have been achieved, then the plan may be abandoned.

8. **Closure of intervention.** Two or three things will bring about closure in a crisis intervention procedure. *First*, the person you are trying to assist may reject your efforts. You cannot force your help on anyone. See if the person will accept help from someone else. If not, express you concern for the distressed person, wish them well and say goodbye. *Second*, you are transferring the person or group to another level of care (hospital, law enforcement agency, other family members, etc.) You should inform the receiving parties about what has happened to the person and what has been done so far. You may also make suggestions as to what you think needs to be done next. Acknowledge the person you were assisting; ask if they need any additional support from you. Then provide reassurance and encouragement and say goodbye. *Third*, in some situations the crisis work that you do is sufficient to bring

the person to a resolution. They get stronger and the indications suggest that they can handle the situation on their own. You should let them know that you see them as noticeably improved and that you believe they can handle things from this point forward. Ask if they think your perceptions are accurate. If they agree, provide contact information if they need additional assistance. Wish them well and say goodbye. Let them know that you will be following up in a few days just to make sure things are working out okay.

NOTE: One exception. If the person you are dealing with is suicidal, you must make sure that they are transferred to appropriate professional care even if they try to reject your help. You cannot leave suicidal people alone. You must engage others to be helpful in the situation. The aim for crisis workers when dealing with a suicidal person is to get others involved in the helping process.

Author's Note: The eight steps of Dr. Albert Roberts general crisis intervention process have been simplified and reduced in number in Dr. George Everly's very practical SAFER-R model for individual crisis intervention. The SAFER-R model is taught in the Assisting Individuals in Crisis course from the International Critical Incident Stress Foundation (ICISF). People who wish to be effective in crisis intervention need to be trained in specific skills for work with individuals and the specialty skills necessary for work with groups. It is highly recommended that you take the course for Assisting Individuals in Crisis if you have not already done so.

*** CRITICAL INFORMATION ***

Critical Incident Stress Management (CISM):

The initials, CISM, serve two key functions. First, they represent the title of a specific crisis intervention program, *Critical Incident Stress Management*, which is a specialized package of crisis intervention techniques that are linked to each other and blended together to alleviate the reactions to traumatic experiences. Some crisis intervention techniques are used to assist individuals. Depending on circumstances, other interventions are applied to homogeneous or heterogeneous groups needing assistance. Individuals and groups have different issues and different needs. We do not use the same intervention techniques for individuals and for groups. Individual techniques serve the needs of individuals. Group techniques were designed for use with groups.

Second, CISM represents a description of a ***comprehensive, integrated, systematic and multi-component*** crisis intervention program. The word *comprehensive* means that there are elements of the crisis intervention program in place before, during and after a traumatic event. *Integrated* simply means that the parts of the CISM program are not used in isolation from each other. Instead they are linked or blended as necessary to provide the very best services to people in crisis. *Systematic* means that there are logical, reasonable steps to take to manage a crisis. Some steps must be accomplished first before others are introduced. *Multi-component* means that no single crisis intervention technique should be used alone to the exclusion of other interventions. One isolated intervention rarely accomplishes the goals of crisis intervention. A program of support services is required to be effective in most cases.

- ***Critical Incident Stress Debriefing (CISD):***

  A CISD is one crisis intervention technique in the field of Critical Incident Stress Management (CISM) among many others. It is not the same as CISM since CISM represents a program and CISD is only one small part of that program.

  A *Critical Incident Stress Debriefing* is a specific, 7-step interactive group crisis intervention designed to assist a *homogeneous group* of people <u>after</u> an exposure to the <u>same significant traumatic event (critical incident)</u>. The CISD is not a stand-alone process and it should never be provided outside of an integrated package of crisis interventions within the Critical Incident Stress Management (CISM) program. ***Under no circumstance should this interactive group crisis intervention tool be considered psychotherapy or a*** *substitute for psychotherapy. It will not cure PTSD once that condition has been established. (PTSD can only be diagnosed after the symptoms have remained for at least a month's time. CISM services should be provided long before PTSD can be diagnosed.) CISD is a support tool designed to enhance unit cohesion and unit performance after a homogeneous groups' exposure to a traumatic event. A CISD is not a cure for any form of mental disorder. <u>It is effective in reducing distress and restoring unit cohesion and unit performance when powerful traumatic event has occurred and when the homogeneous group is distressed by that event. Success in CISD requires a well-trained CISM team including the mental health professional and the peer support personnel. Face to face or telephone follow-up and sometimes referral services are also important for the success of a CISD</u>*

- *CISM in its Proper Context:*

Critical Incident Stress Management is a subset of the much broader field of crisis intervention. CISM shares directly in the *history, theory, principles, practices or intervention tools, and goals of crisis intervention.* Studies, therefore, which evaluated the effectiveness of the goals, principles, and appropriate, well-designed applications of crisis intervention services are also applicable to the field of CISM. It should be noted, however, that CISM is a more focused set of crisis interventions designed specifically to manage the traumatic stress associated with exposure to critical incidents.

* ADDITIONAL INFORMATION *

Milestones in Crisis Intervention

1861 - 1864 ....American Civil War. First formal recognition that soldiers suffer a high stress condition known as "Soldier's Heart." Later it came to be known as acute Posttraumatic Stress Disorder.

1870-71 .... French identify simple steps that reduce stress during the Franco Prussian War. Removal from war stimuli, rest, food, and an opportunity to talk return many to the battlefield.

WWI (1914-1918) .... Thomas Salmon, MD, develops first empirical evidence that early intervention reduces chronic psychiatric morbidity.

WWII (1939-1945) .... Processes of Proximity, Immediacy and Expectancy are identified as important "active ingredients" in effective emergency psychological response. The term, "Psychological First Aid" first used.

1944 .... Erik Lindemann's observations of grief reactions to the Coconut Grove fire begins *modern era* of crisis intervention.

1950's .... Community suicide prevention programs proliferate. Psychological First Aid used in disasters.

1963/64 .... Gerald Caplan's three tiers of preventive psychiatry implemented within the newly generated community mental health system (i.e. primary prevention, secondary prevention, tertiary prevention.)

Late 1960's .... Crisis intervention principles applied to reduce the
early 1970's   need for hospitalization of potentially "chronic" populations.

1974 .... J.T. Mitchell begins early work on crisis and stress in emergency services personnel. First use of the group crisis intervention process known as Critical Incident Stress Debriefing (CISD)

1980 .... Formal nosological recognition of posttraumatic stress disorder (PTSD) in the DSM-III *legitimizes* an examination of crisis and traumatic events as threats to long-term mental health.

1982 .... Air Florida Flight 90 air disaster in Washington, D.C. prompts re-examination of psychological support for emergency response personnel. First large-scale disaster use of the group crisis intervention, Critical Incident Stress Debriefing (CISD) that was originally formulated in 1974.

1986 .... "Violence in the workplace" era begins with the death of 13 postal workers on the job.

1989	Opening of the International Critical Incident Stress Foundation. Now serving the over 1500 CISM teams in 28 nations.
1992	American Red Cross initiates formal training for a nationwide mental health disaster team. Hurricane Andrew puts this concept to the test.
1993	Social Development Office (Amiri Diwan), ICISF, Kuwait University and others implement a nationwide crisis intervention system for post-war Kuwait.
1993	First World Trade Center Bombing
1994	DSM-IV recognizes Acute Stress Disorder
1995	Bombing of the Federal Building in Oklahoma City underscores need for crisis services for rescue personnel, as well as civilians.
1996	TWA 800 air disaster emphasizes the need for emergency mental health services for families of the victims of traumas and disaster.
1996	Aviation Disaster Family Assistance Act.
1997	Gore Commission recommends crisis services for airline industry. ICISF gains United Nations affiliation.
1997	AFI 44-153 mandates establishment of crisis programs for US Air Force bases worldwide.
1998	OSHA 3153-1998 recommends crisis intervention programs for late-night retail stores.
1999	Comdinst 1754.3 requires the establishment of a CISM team for each US Coast Guard region.
1999	DOD DIRECTIVE 6490.5 establishes policy and responsibilities for developing Combat Stress Control (CSC) programs throughout the US military.
1999	Mass shooting in Colorado high school leads to a re-examination of youth school violence issues and an increase in the establishment of school crisis response programs.

2000 ....Increased international concern for nuclear, biological, and / or chemical terrorism includes planning for mental health consequences.

September 11, 2001
.....................................Terrorist attacks against World Trade Center, Pennsylvania and the Pentagon in Washington, DC. Generated an enormous and prolonged (approximately 1 ½ years) crisis intervention response to victims, families, businesses, communities and emergency personnel.

2002 ....NIMH publishes guidelines on Mental Health and Mass Violence. (National Institutes of Mental Health, 2002).

2002 – 2014..................Wars in Afghanistan and Iraq create challenges in military community and combat stress control.

2002 ....EAPA releases guidelines on disaster mental health. (Employee Assistance Professionals Association, 2002).

2004 ....Massive Tsunami hits Indonesia causing catastrophic damage. Critical Incident Stress Management Foundation of Australia (CISMFA), an affiliate of ICISF, tackles the training of crisis responders for South Pacific relief agencies.

2004 ....Four major hurricanes hit Florida and southern USA. Crisis intervention services are challenged by back-to-back storms and the devastation of entire communities throughout Florida.

2005 ....NVOAD (National Volunteer Organizations Active in Disaster) releases recommendations for disaster mental health intervention and training. (Olson, 2005).

2005 ....Hurricanes Katrina and Wilma devastate coastal areas of southern USA and Florida. Approximately 1,300 dead, and many thousands of sick and injured. Over 33,000 aerial evacuations, and 96,000 square miles of severe damage make these storms among the most devastating and costly natural disasters in US history. The also generate significant challenges for all response organizations including those dedicated to crisis intervention services.

2006 ....Fears of pandemic influenza; preparations begin. Crisis intervention services are tapped for guidance on dealing with widespread psychological distress.

2007 ....CISM services are recognized by the General Assembly of the United Nations. A CISM Unit is established under the Department of Safety and Security.

2008 ....Earthquake in China caused the death of 224,000 people. Although some aid groups were allowed in and some used aspects of CISM with the population, the closed nature of the county and the needs of a vast population made relief and recovery work, especially from a mental health perspective, very difficult.

2009 ....Bush fires (wild land) raged across southern Australia with the greatest loss of life in Australian bush fire history. CISM teams were deployed to assist emergency personnel during and after the tragedy.

2010 ....Natural disasters killed nearly a million people in 2010. That equates to more people than all of the victims killed by acts of terrorism in the last 40 years. The greatest killer was the Haiti earthquake in which approximately 225,000 died. CISM services were deployed in earthquakes, fires, floods and tornadoes to support local communities and the emergency services personnel who responded to them.

2011 ....The year of the great Fukushima, earthquake, tsunami, and nuclear power plant disaster. The area sustained a huge loss of life and massive destruction. CISM teams are rare in Japan. At one point a Swedish company sent in outside crisis teams to assist its employees.

2012 ....This year witnessed the horrific mass pediatric murder of 20 first grade children and several of their teachers, their principal and school psychologist. The crisis intervention work of the Connecticut State police will long be remembered for its innovation, its human sensitivity, and its genuineness in the management of the families of the children and the adults who cared so much for them.

2012 ....The impact of Super Storm Sandy kept crisis workers busy for nearly a year. The number of populations served with crisis support services set records in many states.

2013 ....The Boston bombing riveted the nations attention in April 2013. CISM services were very active during and in the aftermath of the terrorist event.

2013 ....Although somewhat overshadowed by the Boston bombing, the fertilizer explosion in West, Texas saw the deployment of regional, state and federal CISM services. Some peer support services have extended beyond a year.

2014 ....A busy year for crisis services. From a record setting cyclone in the Philippines with a tremendous loss of life and overwhelming destruction to mud slides in Oregon, civil unrest in the St. Louis area, and wild land fires in Washington and California. There was little time for crisis support teams to sit back and rest.

2015 ....Paris is attacked twice in one year by terrorists. Nearly 150 people are killed. French crisis teams work long and hard to assist the French population in recovering from the horror.

2015 ....Terror attacks in Chattanooga, Tennessee and San Bernardino produce local and national psychological reactions. CISM teams respond to assist.

2016 ....As the tactics of terror evolve, CISM services are forced to employ support services that must be flexible and adaptive to a wide range of situations.

The above milestones in the field of crisis intervention tell us about the developments and successes of crisis intervention. The list is, by no means, a complete list of tragedies where CISM services were applied. The list helps to guide us through new developments and innovations for future situations where crisis intervention will most likely play an important role.

References

American Psychiatric Association Committee on Civil Defense (1954). Psychological first aid in community disasters. *Journal of the American Medical Association (JAMA),* 156 (1), 36-41.)

Blain, D., Hoch, P., & Ryan, V.G. (1945) A course in Psychological First Aid and Prevention: A preliminary report. *American Journal of Psychiatry,* 101: 629-634.)

Boothby, R. J. G. (1978). *Boothby: Recollections of a rebel.* Chicago, IL; Hutchinson

Dewey, R. (1933). First aid to the newly arriving patient in the public hospital for mental diseases. *American Journal of Psychiatry, 90/*2: 299-301.

Employee Assistance Professionals Association (EAPA). (2002). Report of the disaster preparedness task force, Boston.

National Institutes of Mental Health (2002). Mental Health and Mass Violence. Washington, DC; US Government Printing Office.

Olson, J. (2005). National volunteer organizations active in disaster: Successful strategies for collaboration during the historic 2004 hurricane season. *The Dialogue: A Quarterly Technical Assistance Bulletin on Disaster Behavioral Health* (SAMHSA), Summer 16-17.

Roberts, A. (2005). Crisis intervention handbook, assessment, treatment and research. New York, NY: Oxford University Press

Terr, L. C. (1992). Mini-Marathon Groups: psychological "first aid" following disasters. *Bulletin of the Menniger Clinic. 56*(11) 76-86.

Thorn, F. C. (April 1952). Psychological first aid, *Journal of Clinical Psychology, 8*(2), 210-211.)

Section Two
Stress: Psychological and Behavioral Reactions To Stressors

Something to think about:

"It's not stress that kills us, it is our reaction to it."
- Hans Selye

The core elements of CISM covered in this section are in bold and enlarged letters below:

1. Assessment and Triage of people in crisis
2. Listening skills, The SAFER-R model, and individual crisis intervention
3. Informational group processes
4. Interactive group processes
5. Strategic Planning, Incident assessment, Operations management, *Target, Types, Timing, Theme, and Team*
6. Personal and Community resilience. (Resiliency includes the concepts of *resistance, resilience, and recovery.*)

A Review of Stress Terms
- **Stressor:**
  A stressor is stimulus that causes, or initiates the stress response.

- ***Stress or Stress Response:***
  Stress is a state of arousal in reaction (response) to a stimulus (stressor). It is also a nonspecific response of the body to any demand. Stress consists of a combination of neurologic, neuroendocrine, and endocrine arousal response mechanisms that can alter every organ and function in the human body. Stress accelerates the aging process. *Stress equals arousal.*

- ***Target Organs:***
  The part of the body, or mind, that is a target of the stress and which develops signs and symptoms of over-arousal.

Stressor →	Stress Response →	Target Organ
Example:		
Traffic jam →	Increased Adrenalin → Feelings of Anxiety	Increased heart rate and blood pressure, etc.

- **Burnout:**
  The term 'burnout' was commonly used in the 1980's to describe mounting stress that was not associated with a traumatic event, but was occurring as a result of everyday life. The term lost favor when it was overused as a description of every possible stress condition. The more accurate term, 'Cumulative Stress' describes the buildup of stress over time with harmful consequences such as deterioration in performance, changes in relationships, and deterioration in mental and physical health.

- **Cumulative Stress:**
  Stress arousal that slowly builds up over time. Sometimes it is called _burnout_. The term _burnout_, however, has lost a precise definition as a result of overuse and misuse. Disruptive and dangerous physical and psychological conditions can result from Cumulative Stress because it erodes coping mechanisms.

  The three phases of Cumulative Stress are:
  1. Stress Arousal:
     a. anxiety
     b. panic
     c. difficulty concentrating
     d. feeling out of control or overwhelmed
     e. stress related physical symptoms such as tachycardia, arrhythmias, gastrointestinal distress, rashes, acute elevation in blood pressure, muscle tension, headaches, etc.

  2. Energy Conservation Phase:
     a. Delaying decisions or actions

b. lateness

c. absenteeism

d. increased coffee, tea, soda, tobacco consumption

e. withdrawal, avoidance

3. Exhaustion Phase, which may include:

a. feeling helpless or hopeless

b. fully developed depression

c. serious consideration of changing job status

d. serious consideration of changing personal living situation

e. desire to withdraw and take a 'geographical cure'

f. contemplation of self-destructive actions

g. substance abuse

- *Eustress:*

This is a positive type of stress that can motivate us and it may lead to improved health and performance.

- *Distress:*

This type of stress is negative and it causes discomfort, pain, and even dysfunction. It may lead to the erosion of health and set the stage for disease. It may also interfere with one's ability to perform their professional and personal tasks.

Traumatic Stress

- *Trauma:*

A trauma is any event outside the usual realm of human experience that is markedly distressing (e.g., evokes reactions of intense fear, helplessness, horror, etc.). Such traumatic stressors usually involve the perceived threat to one's own body or to the safety of someone in close proximity.

- ***Traumatic Stress:***
  Traumatic Stress is described as a broad range of cognitive, physical, emotional, spiritual, or behavioral *reactions* to a traumatic event. The term, traumatic stress, is loosely defined as a general, overall reaction in individuals or in groups after an exposure to a traumatic stressor.

- ***Post-Traumatic Stress:***
  Post-Traumatic Stress is a very intense arousal in response to the traumatic stressor (trauma). Traumatic stress overwhelms coping mechanisms leaving individuals out of control and feeling helpless. Sometimes those feelings may cause fear and, as a result, they may reject help because they think that they cannot be helped. (Sometimes Post Traumatic Stress is referred to as "Critical Incident Stress.")

- ***Post-Traumatic Stress Disorder (PTSD):***
  This term is applied as the official diagnosis of a post-traumatic stress syndrome that occurs after exposure to a traumatic event and is characterized by symptoms of:
  1. excessive excitability and arousal
  2. numbing withdrawal, and avoidance
  3. repetitive, intrusive memories or recollections of the trauma
  4. duration of at least 1 month
  5. significant distress / dysfunction as well as disruption to normal life pursuits

- ***Criteria for Post-Traumatic Stress Disorder:***
- A. Exposure to actual or threatened death, serious injury, or sexual violence.
- B. Presence of one (or more) symptoms of intrusion associated with the traumatic event.
- C. Persistent avoidance of stimuli associated with the trauma and beginning the traumatic event.
- D. Negative alterations in cognitions and mood associated with the traumatic event and beginning or worsening after the traumatic event

- E. Marked alterations in arousal and reactivity associated with the traumatic event and beginning after or worsening after the traumatic event.
- F. Duration of disturbance (B, C, D, and E) is more than 1 month.
- G. The disturbance causes clinically significant distress or impairment in social, occupational and other important areas of functioning.
- H. The disturbance is not attributable to physiologic effects of a substance (e.g., medication or alcohol) or other medical condition.

- *Psycho-traumatology:*
  This term is applied to the study of psychological trauma, more specifically, the factors antecedent to, concomitant with, and subsequent to psychological traumatization. (Everly & Lating, 1995)

- *Trauma Membrane:*
  J. Lindy developed the concept of a "trauma membrane." He believed that a person forms a psychological protective barrier once they have been traumatized. This barrier helps to protect individuals from subsequent traumatic exposures. It insulates people from continued intrusion or overstimulation. There is, however, a down side to the development of a trauma membrane. It may also insulate people from efforts by others to assist in their recovery. They may not, for example, put much belief in their own recovery. They may not request legitimate assistance or they may keep their expectations very low to avoid becoming overly optimistic. In this way, they avoid being vulnerable to disappointment or frustration by the lack of action on the part of other people. The trauma membrane 'thickens' with time; therefore early intervention after trauma or a disaster is highly recommended.

Early Psychological Intervention
State of the Art

** IMPORTANT INFORMATION **

For Understanding Stress Concepts

In 2002, the National Institutes of Mental Health stated in its *Mental Health and Mass Violence* report:

A.) Most survivors of disasters and violence should experience a normal recovery, but there is a rationale for providing early psychological intervention to those in need.

B.) Interventions should be part of a phasic, integrated, and multi-component system.
   1. Follow-up services should be considered for:
      a) The bereaved.
      b) Those with pre-existing psychiatric disorders.
      c) Those requiring medical or surgical intervention.
      d) Those with acute stress disorder.
      e) Those for whom the exposure was especially chronic or intense.
      f) Those who request assistance.

C.) Early intervention services may be implemented by mental health professionals, the clergy, medical and nursing professionals, para-professionals, and community volunteers.

Symptoms of Distress
(Bold Indicates More Severe)

1. ***Cognitive (intellectual processes) Distress***
   a. Sensory distortion
   b. Difficulty remembering details
   c. Disorientation to surroundings
   d. **Confusion (efforts at "dumbing down" terms)**
   e. **Inability to concentrate**
   f. **Difficulty in decision-making**
   g. **Difficulty in problem solving**
   h. Guilt

i. Preoccupation (obsessions) with event
j. **Inability to understand consequences of behavior**
k. **Suicidal / homicidal thoughts**
l. **Psychosis**

2. *Emotional Distress*
   a. Anxiety
   b. Anger
   c. Irritability
   d. Intense sadness
   e. **Panic (often associated with self-medication)**
   f. **Vegetative depression*(see below)**
   g. Fear, phobia, phobic avoidance
   h. Post-traumatic stress (PTS)
   i. Grief (Mourning is associated with the death of a person or the loss of a cherished object or the loss of marriage through divorce. It may also be associated feelings of the loss of a safe world.)
   j. **Pathological Grief** when:
      1) Associated with severe guilt
      2) Lasts well beyond reasonable time frame
      3) So intense as to impair ability to function
      * **Vegetative depression** (depressed mood plus)
         1. **Decreased appetite**
         2. **Decreased energy**
         3. **Decreased sleep**
         4. **Decreased libido desire for sexual contact with spouse**
         5. **Predicts PTSD when it is peri-traumatic (around the trauma. That is, it is seen as closely connected to the traumatic event.)**
         6. **Associated with self-medication**

3. *Behavioral Distress*
   a. Becoming unusually impulsive
   b. **Risk-taking**
   c. Excessive eating
   d. **Alcohol / substance use abuse to control stress**

e. Hyper startle (excessively responsive to loud noises and sudden movements.)
f. Compensatory sexuality
g. Compensatory purchasing
h. Compulsivity
i. Sleep disturbance
j. Withdrawal
k. Family discord
l. Crying spells
m. Hyper-vigilance
n. 1000-yard stare (unnatural staring into the distance)
o. Violence
p. Anti-social Behaviors

4. *Physical Distress*
a. Tachycardia (fast heart), Bradycardia (slow heart)
b. Headaches
c. Hyperventilation
d. Muscle spasms
e. Thirst / dry mouth
f. Psychogenic sweating (sweating caused by fear)
g. Fatigue / exhaustion
h. Vague muscle aches or body pains
i. Indigestion / nausea / vomiting
j. Visual distortions
k. Blood in stools, sputum, vomit, urine
l. Chest pain
m. Difficulty breathing
n. Loss of consciousness

5. *Spiritual Distress*
a. Anger at your God
b. Loss of belief in a just world
c. Loss of a sense of purpose
d. Doubts about the existence of a benign God
e. Belief that one has been abandoned by God
f. Withdrawal from faith community / cessation of faith-related practices Crisis Intervention
g. Hallucinations of a religious / spiritual nature

Suggested Readings

American Psychiatric Association (1964). *First aid for psychological reactions in disasters.* Washington, DC: American Psychiatric Association.

Artiss, K. (1963). Human behavior under stress: From combat to social psychiatry. *Military Medicine, 128,* 1011-1015.

Bohl, N. (1995). Measuring the effectiveness of CISD. *Fire Engineering,* 125-126.

Boscarino, J. A., Adams, R. E. & Figley, C. R. (2005). A prospective cohort study of the effectiveness of employer-sponsored crisis interventions after a major disaster. *International Journal of Emergency Mental Health, 7*(1), 31-44

British Psychological Working Party (1990). *Psychological aspects of disaster.* Leicester, UK: British Psychological Society.

Caplan, G. (1961). *An approach to community mental health.* New York: Grune and Stratton.

Caplan, G. (1964). *Principles of preventive psychiatry.* New York: Basic Books.

Caplan, G. (1969). Opportunities for school psychologists in the primary prevention of mental health disorders in children, In A. Bindman and A. Spiegel (Eds.) *Perspectives in community mental health* (pp.420-436). Chicago: Aldine.

Deahl, M., Srinivasan, M., Jones, N., Thomas, J., Neblett, C., & Jolly, A. (2000). Preventing psychological trauma in soldiers. The role of operational stress training and psychological debriefing. *British Journal of Medical Psychology, 73,* 77-85.

Everly, G. S. Jr. & Lating, J. M. (1995). *Psychotraumatology: Key papers and core concepts in post-traumatic stress.* New York, NY: Plenum.

Everly, G. S., Jr. & Mitchell, J. T. (1997). *Critical incident stress management: A new era and standard of care in crisis intervention.* Ellicott City, MD: Chevron Publishing Corp.

Everly G. S. & Mitchell, J. T. (1998). *Assisting individuals in crisis: A workbook.* Ellicott City, MD: International Critical Incident Stress Foundation.

Everly, G. S., Jr. (1999). Emergency mental health: An overview. *International Journal of Emergency Mental Health, 1,* 3-7.

Everly, G. S., Jr. & Mitchell, J. T. (1999). *Critical incident stress management: A new era and standard of care in crisis intervention, second edition.* Ellicott City, MD: Chevron Publishing Corp.

Kardiner, A., & Spiegel, H. (1947). *War, stress, and neurotic illness.* New York: Hoeber.

Lindemann, E. (1944). Symptomatology and management of acute grief. *American Journal of Psychiatry, 101,* 141-148.

Lindy, J. (1985). The trauma membrane and other clinical concepts derived from psychotherapeutic work with survivors of natural disasters. *Psychiatric Annals, 15,* 153-160.

Mitchell, J. T., & Resnik, H. L. P. (1986). *Emergency response to crisis.* Ellicott City, MD: Chevron Publishing (reprinted from original, 1981).

Mitchell, J. T. (2003). Major misconceptions in crisis intervention. *International Journal of Emergency Mental Health, 5*(4), 185-197.

Mitchell, J. T. (2004). Characteristics of successful early intervention programs. *International Journal of Emergency Mental Health, 6*(4). 175-184.

Mitchell, J. T., & Everly, G. S., Jr. (2001). *Critical incident stress management: Basic group crisis interventions.* Ellicott City, MD: International Critical Incident Stress Foundation.

Neil, T., Oney, J., DiFonso, L., Thacker, B., & Reichart, W. (1974). *Emotional first aid.* Louisville, KY: Kemper-Behavioral Science Associates.

Parad, H. J. (1971). Crisis intervention. In R. Morris (Ed.) *Encyclopedia of Social Work, 1,* 196-202.

Richards, D. (2001). A field study of critical incident stress debriefing versus critical incident stress management. *Journal of Mental Health, 10,* 351-362.

Roberts, A. R. (2005) Bridging the past and present to the future of crisis intervention and crisis management. In A.R. Roberts (Ed.) *Crisis intervention handbook: Assessment, treatment, research.* New York, NY: Oxford University Press.

Salmon, T. S. (1919). War neuroses and their lesson. *New York Medical Journal, 108,* 993-994.

Slaikeu, K. A. (1984). *Crisis intervention: A handbook for practice and research.* Boston, MA: Allyn and Bacon, Inc.

Solomon, Z., and Benbenishty, R. (1986). The role of proximity, immediacy, and expectancy in frontline treatment of combat stress reaction among Israelis in the Lebanon War. *American Journal of Psychiatry, 143,* 613-617.

Stierlin, E. (1909). *Psycho-neuropathology as a result of a mining disaster March 10, 1906.* Zurich: University of Zurich.

Section Three
Strategic Planning in Crisis Intervention and Critical Incident Stress Management

Something to think about:

"The psychological states of emergency response personnel can have a direct effect on the mental and physical health of survivors of a trauma or a disaster" A. J. Glass.

Part of the strategy in CISM is to maintain the health of the providers so that the survivors gain some benefits as well.

The core elements of CISM covered in this section are in bold and enlarged letters below:

1. Assessment and Triage of people in crisis
2. Listening skills, The SAFER-R model, and individual crisis intervention.
3. Informational group processes.
4. Interactive group processes.
5. **Strategic Planning, Incident assessment, Operations management, Target, Types, Timing, Theme, and Team**
6. Personal and Community resilience. (Resiliency includes the concepts of resistance, resilience, and recovery.

For understanding strategic planning for CISM

Strategic Planning for Effective Staff Support:

Staff support is a program of support services for the personnel of an organization. These programs work best when they are already established and functioning well before a traumatic event occurs. They are impossible to develop in the midst of a chaotic and traumatic situation. If a support program does not exist before the traumatic event occurs, it is best to call in trained personnel from another locality who can assist in the current crisis. After the crisis situation is resolved, then efforts should be made to develop an internal crisis support program. Even small steps toward the development of a staff support programs can be helpful in managing a future crisis especially if there are links to a network of support teams in other areas of the country. Whether the support is coming from a local team or a team from elsewhere that has been called in to assist, the following list of tasks can be very helpful in deciding what needs to be done during the situation.

1. Start the assessment process by looking at a) **nature and magnitude of the situation** and the b) **impact on the personnel**.
2. Think before reacting. Think strategic planning.
3. Decide if individual or group services, or both, will be required. Will people need information (informational groups) or will they need to sit down in a homogeneous interactive group of people with the same experience and discuss the situation and their reactions.
4. Work out a strategic crisis plan before providing crisis intervention.
5. Make sure you provide follow-up and referral services

*** CRITICAL INFORMATION ***

For Developing and Applying Strategic Crisis Support

This section focuses on *Strategic Planning* since it is one of the most important, but frequently most neglected, elements of Critical Incident Stress Management. Crisis management teams have sometimes responded to traumatic situations with a _knee jerk_ reaction. That is, they try to apply crisis intervention tactics before considering if they are choosing the right tactics or if they have the right resources to respond to the crisis. A poorly developed operational strategy generates inappropriate or misguided tactics.

The crisis strategy, of course, is the big picture. It is characterized by:

1. **Assessment of the circumstances**
2. **Development of clear goals and objectives**
3. **Selection of the most skillful people to provide the services**
4. **Development of a strategic plan of action.**
5. **Selection of a specific set of crisis tactics that are most likely to successfully carry out the strategic plan.**

A comprehensive, integrated, systematic, multi-tactic approach (CISM) that blends the tactics has the best chance of assisting people through the crisis experience. <u>Comprehensive</u> = a total support package that contains techniques that are used before, during, and after an incident. Integrated = techniques are blended and combined together. Systematic = techniques applied in a logical order. Multi-component = many different techniques within the program.

Strategic Planning Formula:

There is a simple formula that can be used to develop the strategic plan when intervening in any emotionally charged event.

Assess these issues:

Theme (What elements of the incident are causing the greatest distress to those involved? What will influence the decisions the team makes to provide support?)

- What has happened? What is the nature of the event?
- How awful or serious is the event?
- What are the threats?

Target(s) (Who are the people who are affected by the critical incident?)

- Who is involved in the incident? How many people?
- What is the impact on the personnel?
- Individuals?

- Heterogeneous collection of people?
- Are there identifiable homogeneous groups?

Types (What CISM tools would be most helpful in the current circumstances?)
- What support services are most likely to be helpful under the circumstances?
- Individual?
- Informational groups?
- Process groups?
- Family / significant other support
- Organizational support
- Follow-up services
- Referrals

Timing (Decisions must be made to arrange the timing of CISM services to meet the needs of those in a state of crisis)
- When should the various types of interventions be instituted?
- Sequential order?
- Separately?
- Simultaneously?
- Blended
- All at once?

Team (who is going to carry out the CISM services?)
- Do you have the right team member(s) to match the needs of those in need of assistance?
- Team experienced?
- Team cohesive?
- Team appropriate?
- Sufficient number of team responders?
- Any special skills required by team members?
- Matched to the profession(s) of those impacted by the trauma?
- Team available for the length of time required?

Additional Details on the "Five-T" Formula:

1. **Themes.** Make sure you have a full understanding of the threats, issues, concerns, and facts about the incident itself and the services that may have already been provided. Themes are anything that influences decision-making or the choice of interventions. They must be considered throughout the crisis intervention. Review the Target, Type, Timing aspects of the strategic plan before instituting the slate of interventions.
2. **Target.** Figure out which individuals or possibly groups might need psychological first aid. There may be several target populations requiring assistance.
3. **Type.** Determine which types of interventions are going to be most appropriate for this particular crisis and for the specific targets under the circumstances.
4. **Timing.** Next, decide when the various interventions are most likely to be helpful. The best help at the wrong time will most certainly be rejected or useless.
5. **Team.** Who is selected to provide the support services? Are you sending in a team or an individual from a team who has the ability to be most helpful? Carefully choose the best resources available to provide the services you worked out while looking at the target, type, timing and themes of the situation as you developed your strategic plan.

"Strategy without tactics is the slowest route to victory. Tactics without strategy is the noise before defeat"

- Sun Tzu -

Tactical Components of CISM:

A successful crisis support program contains a package of tactics, procedures, or interventions. This important characteristic frequently appears in the crisis intervention literature. The very first article on crisis intervention programs for emergency personnel listed numerous components that were required for a reasonably comprehensive stress management program (Mitchell, 1983). The British Psychological

Society (1990) stated that crisis intervention programs must be multi-component in nature. More recently, the National Institutes of Mental Health confirmed the multi-component nature of early intervention programs (2002). Most CISM programs contain twelve primary components or 'tactics.' They are:

1. Pre-event preparation, education, training, planning, and policy development.
2. Assessment procedures
3. Strategic planning procedures
4. Individual crisis intervention support actions
5. On-scene support services (advice and consultation to supervisors, assistance to individuals acutely impacted by the traumatic event and care for primary victims until other resources are mobilized.)
6. Supportive and informational Rest, Information, and Transition Services (RITS) {formerly known as "demobilization'} of large groups of staff members or operations personnel after a disaster
7. Crisis Management Briefing (CMB) – Generally CMB are informational sessions for heterogeneous (mixed or diverse) groups. They are one form of group crisis intervention. Also, the CMB informational sessions are used for various populations and group sizes particularly if there are large numbers gathered together in one area.
8. Immediate Defusing, on the same day as the incident, for homogeneous (similar) groups who have had about the same level of exposure to a traumatic event.
9. Critical Incident Stress Debriefing (CISD) for homogeneous (similar) groups several days after their exposure to the same traumatic event.
10. Significant other support services (family support, education, individual support, group support, etc.)
11. Follow-up services (phone calls, visits to the work site, group meetings, individual consultations, etc.)
12. Referral services for those who need more assistance

In reality, there can be more components of a CISM program than those listed above. Many CISM programs, for example, have a chaplain/clergy crisis intervention component added to their list.

Crisis programs with only one or two components would not be categorized as a comprehensive, integrated, systematic or multi-tactic program. Such a program can only provide a minimum of services. The title, CISM, is typically only applied when a program is providing crisis support work and utilizing seven or more components in its package of interventions (Mitchell and Everly, 2001).

*** CRITICAL INFORMATION ***

Detailed information on The Critical Incident Stress Debriefing (CISD) will be presented in Section Seven of this book. Since it was mentioned as one of the tactics in the Tactical Components of CISM segment above, it is worthwhile to clarify the definition here before moving on. The Critical Incident Stress Debriefing (CISD) is a specific group crisis support process that focuses on enhancing unit cohesion and unit performance. It should <u>not</u> be used for any crisis event unless these three primary criteria for an interactional group crisis intervention can be verified:

1. **The group must be clearly a homogeneous group (the group members know each other, work closely together, have very similar job responsibilities, and the same leadership). A homogeneous group should have the following crucial characteristics: a) an established relationship with each other, b) sufficient time together so as to be thought of as if one unified whole, c) a shared history including roughly the same exposure to the traumatic event.**
2. **The mission must be complete or it has moved beyond the acute phases of the crisis event.**
3. **The level of traumatic exposure should be about equal for the group members.**

Critical Incident Stress Debriefings are restricted to applications with homogeneous groups. They tend to be the more complicated of the CISM interventions. They need considerably more detailed information than is being offered here. That is why an entire section of this book has been put aside for the CISD process. This course teaches in an order that goes from the simpler techniques to the more complex. The CISD is among the most complex of CISM tactics. Let's not get ahead of ourselves at this point. We have much to cover before we get into the CISD process.   It will definitely be covered.

Note: The chart on the next two pages contains

*** CRITICAL INFORMATION ***

Summary of Commonly Used Crisis Intervention Tactics

Intervention / Tactic	Timing	Target Group	Potential Goals
Pre–event Planning/Preparation	Prior to exposures to traumatic events	Anticipated target or even victim populations	Resistance building. Enhance resiliency anticipatory guidance
Assessment	Pre-intervention	Those directly and indirectly exposed	Determine need for intervention
Strategic planning	Pre-event / early stages of event	Actual and anticipated exposed populations	Improve overall crisis response
Individual Crisis Intervention (includes "Psychological First Aid")	Whenever needed	Individuals as needed	Assessment, screening, education, reduction of acute distress, triage, referral
Informational groups: a) Rest Information Transition Services (RITS) {formerly known as "demobilization"}	Operation shift disengagement Ongoing large scale events As needed	Emergency operations personnel	Decompression, ease transition, screening, triage, guidance, meet basic needs Respite, refreshment preliminary support
b) Crisis Management Briefings Large Group "psychological First Aid"	During or after event.	Any size group needing information, guidance, instructions. Large heterogeneous groups	Information, rumor control, increase cohesion, lower tension and anxiety in the group. Enhance appropriate behaviors
Informational session for small sized group crisis intervention (conversational somewhat similar to a CMB but with only a few people)	During and after the event May be repeated as needed May use the CMB format even though the group size is quite small	Community groups seeking information and resources. Usually non-emergency groups. Often heterogeneous 3-6 in attendance	Provide information, control rumors, reduce acute distress, increase cohesion, facilitate resilience, screening and triage

Summary of Commonly Used Crisis Intervention Tactics

Intervention / Tactic	Timing	Target Group	Potential Goals
Interactive Groups: a) Defusing (group "psychological first aid") b) Critical Incident Stress Debriefing	Up to 8 to 12 hours after the event Post event 24-72 hours – ideal sometimes 5 -10 days. Longer times after disaster (3-4 weeks)	Homogeneous groups only: usually small unit-sized groups; same exposure to the traumatic event Homogeneous groups only with equal trauma exposure (workgroups, teams)	Stabilization, ventilation, reduction of acute distress, screening, information, increase cohesion and facilitate resilience Restore unit cohesion and unit performance
Family crisis intervention	Pre-event preparation Post event support as needed	Families of victims as well as Emergency personnel	Wide range of interventions Preparation CMB, individual, other as needed
Organizational / community intervention, consultation	Pre event preparation Support post event as needed	Organizations, businesses, agencies impacted by trauma	Improve preparedness and response. Leadership guidance. Assist in recovery
Pastoral Crisis Intervention	Before, during, after as needed	Individual, RITS, defusing, CMB, faith based crisis intervention	Faith-Based support
Follow-up / Referral	Some follow-up is always necessary; Referrals as needed	Intervention recipients, other exposed individuals and groups	Assure continuity of care. Refer as necessary

Characteristics of Effective Staff Support Programs

1. Every successful crisis-oriented emergency services staff support program is **comprehensive**. That is, it has elements in place before, during, and after traumatic events. Additionally, it is **programmatic**. That is, administration must accept a staff support program as a separate entity and build it into the fabric of the organization. Although they remain independent units, staff support programs must communicate, coordinate, and link their efforts with the administration, human services, employee assistance and psychological resources within an organization. It is also quite common for staff support programs to _borrow_ skilled professionals from those resources during crisis situations.

2. Obviously, referrals for additional care or psychotherapy are made to those professionals, but staff support programs work best when the differences between _support_ and _therapy_ are clearly recognized. Staff support services function at peak performance when they function separately under the umbrella of _operations support_. A crisis intervention program for staff is a support function, not so much a management function or a psychotherapeutic function.

3. Well-developed emergency services staff support programs to manage crises are **integrated**. All of the elements of a program are interrelated and blended with one another. The combined effects of an integrated program are far more powerful than any single element.

4. Emergency services personnel are best sustained by a **systematic** program or _support package_, which has phases, segments, or logical steps. Organizations with staff support programs should, therefore, take a few simple steps such as, resting personnel and talking with them on an individual basis, before increasing the complexity, number, and duration of the available staff support functions after a distressing event.

5. Effective staff support programs must be ***multi-tactic*** in approach. Many different types of support services must be available since every person will have a somewhat different response to a highly stressful event. Each person will have different requirements to help them recover from their stress.

6. Although it is part of a Comprehensive, Integrated, Systematic and Multi-tactic (CISM) approach, ***linkage to a wide range of resources*** is an important enough tactic that it be presented here as one of the key characteristics of any staff support program. The magnitudes of some events are so severe, or the personal reactions of some personnel are so intense, that additional assistance may be necessary. An emergency services staff support program must have mental health resources or other types of services within easy access for people who need more help beyond crisis intervention.

7. Among emergency services organizations, such as emergency medical services agencies, fire services and police departments, crisis support teams are most effective when they are run and staffed by ***peer support personnel*** and backed up by both mental health professionals and chaplains who are trained in Critical Incident Stress Management (CISM) (Mitchell, 2004).

References

Benjamin, R., & Carroll, S. J. (1998). *Breaking the social contract: The fiscal crisis in California higher education.* Santa Monica, CA: RAND: Council for Aid to Education.

British Psychological Working Party (1990). *Psychological aspects of disaster.* Leicester, UK: British Psychological Society.

Glass, A. J. (1954). Psychological first aid in community disaster. *Journal of the American Medical Association, JAMA, 156*(1), 36-41)

Gouillart, F. (1995). The day the music died. *Journal of Business Strategy, 16*(3), 14-20.

Hax, A. C., & Majluf, N. S. (1996). *The strategy concept and process, A pragmatic approach.* Upper Saddle River, NJ: Prentice Hall.

Hill, C. W., & Jones, G. R. (1992). *Strategic management: An integrated approach.* Boston, MA: Houghton Mifflin Company.

Liedtka, J. M. (1998 September – October 26). Linking strategic thinking with strategic planning. *Strategy and Leadership,* 30-36.

Mintzberg, H. (1994). *The rise and fall of strategic planning.* New York: The Free Press.

Mitchell, J. T. (1983). When disaster strikes... the critical incident stress debriefing process. *Journal of Emergency Medical Services, 8*(1), 36-39.

Mitchell, J. T. (2006). *Strategic response to crisis.* Ellicott City, MD: International Critical Incident Stress Foundation.

Mitchell, J. T., & Everly, G. S. Jr. (2001). *Critical incident stress debriefing: An operations manual for CISD defusing and other group crisis intervention services, 3rd ed.* Ellicott City, MD: Chevron

NIMH (2002). *Mental health and mass violence: evidence-based early psychological intervention for victims/survivors of mass violence: A workshop to reach consensus on best practices. A report.* National Institutes of Mental Health. Washington, DC: Government Printing Office.

Rowley, D. J., Lujan, H. D., & Dolence, M. G. (1997). *Strategic change in colleges and universities.* San Francisco, CA: Jossey-Bass Publishers.

Traib, J. (1997 October 20 and 27). Drive-thru U: Higher education for people who mean business. *The New Yorker*, 114-123.

Wall, S. J., & Wall, S. R. (1995). The evolution (not the death) of strategy. *Organizational Dynamics, 24,* 2, 6.

Section Four
Informational Group Crisis Interventions

Something to think about:

"More information is always better than less. When people know the reason things are happening, even if it's bad news, they can adjust their expectations and react accordingly. Keeping people in the dark only serves to stir negative emotions." - Simon Sinek, British writer.

The core elements of CISM covered in this section are in bold and enlarged letters below:

1. Assessment and Triage of people in crisis
2. Listening skills, The SAFER-R model, and individual crisis intervention.
3. **Informational group processes.**
4. Interactive group processes.
5. Strategic Planning, Incident assessment, Operations management, Target, Types, Timing, Theme, and Team
6. Personal and Community resilience. (Resiliency includes the concepts of resistance, resilience, and recovery.)

*** CRITICAL INFORMATION ***

Rest, Information, and Transition Services (RITS)

- *RITS* was formerly known as *demobilization*. The name change occurred as a result of requests from both the United Nations and from a number of military services. The requests were made because UN peacemakers and military forces use the word demobilization with a very different meaning than we in the CISM community. Only the label changed, but the process remains the same.

- *RITS* are designed for staff, <u>not</u> for citizen populations outside of emergency services, hospitals, or the military.

- *RITS* are provided for emergency personnel, one time only, at the end of a unit's first exposure to a major incident in which the majority of on duty operations personnel were working under intensely stressful conditions and sometimes for a prolonged period of time. The RITS are not a stand-alone intervention. Some form of follow-up is usually required.

- *RITS* were developed to support emergency personnel who work at large, complex, and prolonged operations. They are typically provided immediately after _emergency operation personnel_ have been released from their _first shift_ at a large-scale incident such as _disaster, a terrorist attack, a wild land fire, or a major search operation_.

- A *RITS* consists of two main segments. The first is a brief *information presentation* of no more than 10 minutes. The second segment is the provision of rest, food, and other refreshments. In most cases, 20 minutes is allotted for the rest and food segment. Then someone from administration or command informs the emergency personnel if they are being released to go home or if they are being reassigned to other duties away from the disaster site or whatever large-scale incident they are working.

- Since the *RITS* is an informational group, only one provider is necessary. There is no effort to engage the participants in a discussion. The objective of RITS is to provide information and instructions. Information, by itself, can be a powerful tool in the reduction of distress.

Rest, Information, and Transition Services

Definition: Quick informational and rest session applied when operations units have been released from service at a major incident such as a disaster that requires a huge commitment of resources. The RITS serves a secondary function as a screening opportunity to assure that individuals who may need assistance are identified after the traumatic event and given the appropriate resources.

Length of time: 10 minutes of information from a crisis team member; 20 minutes of food and rest.

Best Applied: Immediately after work teams have been released from the major incident and before personnel are released to home or normal duties.

Target: Teams of workers. Engine or truck companies, ambulance units, perimeter control teams, search teams, search dog teams, squads, investigation teams, special units, etc. Each work team receives its own RITS session.

Provided By: Trained Critical Incident Stress Team member only.

Location of RITS: Two large rooms. One room is used to provide the information sessions in small work groups. The other room is used to serve food and allow the work crews to rest. The facility should be near enough to the scene to be convenient to gather the crews when they have been released from the scene.

Goals:
- Assess wellbeing of personnel after the major incident
- Mitigate impact of event
- Provide stress management information to personnel
- Provide an opportunity for rest and food before returning to routine duties.
- Assess need for group or individual support services.
- Provide referrals to anyone who might need them.

Process:
- Establish an appropriate RITS center
- Check in units as they arrive
- Keep work teams together
- Assign a stress team member to provide information to the groups
- Limit the information section to ten minutes
- Provide twenty minutes of rest and food
- Let participants know if a CISD is planned
- Provide a handout on stress control suggestions

Contraindications:
- Not for use with routine events.
- Not for use on small-sized events.
- Not a substitute for a CISD.
- Not applied in the case of a line of duty death. A five phase CISD (taught in the advanced group course) is provided in the event of an emergency services death.
- The RITS should be reserved for large-scale events like disasters.
- If a homogeneous operations group has been particularly traumatized by a traumatic event, **excluding** a line of-duty death, a defusing would be the better choice of interventions as long as the personnel are not too weary. (In a line-of-duty death situation, the defusing would be the wrong choice of interventions. A five phase CISD would be more helpful. It is briefly described in Section Five.)

- If they are too weary, just provide a shorter RITS process and let the crews rest.
- Additional interventions such as the CISD can be provided in the next few days.
- Other than the presenter, no one has to speak in a RITS.
- A person attending a RITS can speak if they want to, but *no one is required to speak or answer questions.*
- Work groups from different professions are usually not mixed together during a RITS.

RITS Components
- Check in the units as they arrive.
- A CISM team member gives a 10-minute talk on stress survival skills:
- Describe typical reactions
- List signals of distress
- Provide brief suggestions on controlling stress reactions
- Invite anyone who wishes to speak or ask a question to do so (rarely will anyone speak in a RITS)
- In a separate room provide food and rest for at least twenty minutes until they are released or reassigned by command or supervisors.
- At the end of the food and rest session a command or supervisory person advises the personnel whether they will be released to home or reassigned to other duties.

Presentation Points for RITS:
- Speaker introduces him- or herself.
- Brief review of RITS process. A statement that the speaker is only going to take ten minutes to provide some important information that may prevent stress or help personnel to cope with it faster and easier. A prolonged mission (e.g., a military operation) may require a longer information segment, but certainly never longer than 20 minutes.

- State that some may have symptoms now, others may encounter them later, and some may not develop symptoms at all.
- Provide assurance that stress symptoms are normal under the circumstances.
- Provide a warning not to ignore stress symptoms since they can become dangerous or disruptive if ignored.
- List common cognitive, physical, emotional and behavioral signs and symptoms of stress.
- Provide specific advice on eating, resting, avoiding alcohol and drugs, conversing with loved ones, coping with the media, and other helpful hints to recover from stress.
- Announce the dates and times of support services like the CISD.
- Ask if anyone has any questions or comments. (Few people ever speak in a RITS).
- Summarize the information section.
- Distribute any handout material.

Key concepts:

- For major events only
- Follow-up with CISD
- RITS are provided by trained CISM team members
- Do not provide RITS in the immediate vicinity of the incident
- RITS do not require a mental health professional
- One work team after another is processed until all have received the RITS
- At least 6 hours should pass before personnel return to the scene of the disaster
- Keep the information brief. More can be done later
- Encourage communication with loved ones
- Encourage personnel to call for help if necessary
- Provide individual crisis intervention when necessary
- Do not forget supervisors and command staff. They may need help too

- Encourage proper diet, exercise, rest, and sleep
- Encourage the avoidance of alcohol, nicotine, and drugs
- Be familiar with the RITS so it runs smoothly
- Have supervisory personnel describe the next steps

*** CRITICAL INFORMATION ***

Crisis Management Briefing (CMB)

- CMB is a very versatile group support process for **heterogeneous groups**. Unlike the Rest, Information, and Transition Services, a disaster is not necessary to initiate a CMB. The process can be used with any event that has a significant impact on a community (e.g. a gruesome murder in small community that upsets the majority of the town's inhabitants).
- CMBs have been provided to schools, businesses, church groups, community groups, organizations, clubs, hospitals and governmental agencies.
- A CMB session can be provided multiple times to assure that the same information is distributed to everyone in the community.
- CMBs can be provided by means of television and radio programs. Face-to-face meetings with community members are not always necessary. This flexibility in the approach to providing community members with information is particularly important in times of civil unrest or when there is a serious potential that people could be exposed to bio or chemical hazards by meeting together.
- CMBs can be provided at regular intervals during a disaster as long as new information is provided in each subsequent meeting.
- CMBs are used with military and emergency services personnel who are returning repeatedly to work in a large scale, multi-day event.
- Although it is possible that some communities might require more detailed information in a CMB session lasting an hour or an hour and a quarter, the majority of CMBs are completed in 20 to 30 minutes.

Applications of the Crisis Management Briefing.

Definition

An informational group crisis intervention technique for heterogeneous (mixed) groups or large groups (possibly up to 300 people in the same session in some circumstances.) It may be implemented with civilians after disasters or other large-scale events. It has been utilized in school events, in businesses and industry, in community and church groups. It also may be used with emergency and military groups in the second day of operations and beyond.

Applications:

Terrorism events, disasters, community violence, school crises, work place, and military crises.

Length of Time:

Typically 20-45 minutes (depending on the needs, responses and questions of the group).

Goals:

1) <u>Provide information, guidance, and instructions</u>
2) Rumor control
3) Reduction of chaos
4) Provide suggestions about coping
5) Facilitate follow-up care
6) Provide referral information for those who need more extensive care
7) Promote community cohesion
8) Enhance community morale
9) Assess further needs of the group members
10) Restore people to adaptive functions

Providers:

A two-person team typically presents the CMB. The team members should meet in advance and determine what needs to be covered in the CMB session. They may prepare an outline of their presentation. One presenter is from the CISM team. The other is drawn from the community. The second team member may be a ranking police or fire service official or someone from the health services or a governmental official. In business or industry the team member may be a president or vice president of the firm. In a church it might be the pastor and in a school it might be the principal. In any case the second team member should be a credible representative of the organization with sufficient authority to make important, immediate decisions.

Process:

Step 1: Assemble participants (as much as possible by natural groups – family members, friends, neighbors, or communities)

Step 2: Provide facts regarding the current crisis situation

Step 3: Discuss and normalize common behavioral / Psychological reactions

Step 4: Discuss personal stress management suggestions and guidelines. Also suggest actions that might assist the overall community. Finally, let the participants know about other resources that they may find helpful.

Note:

CMB usually have one or two question and answer periods. Some teams will have a question period after Step 2 and another after Step 4. The majority of CMB teams prefer to have only one question period after Step 4. A single question period keeps the flow of the meeting moving smoothly and avoids diversions away from the most important information. It is the recommended approach.

CMB Frequency: CMBs may be presented only once during a large-scale incident _or_ they may be given at specific time intervals (e.g., 7:30 a.m. and 7:30 p.m.) _or_ they may be given on an as- needed basis. They may be repeated, but new information must be added in each session. Many times different teams will present CMBs when the situation is a prolonged operation.

Follow-up: The follow-up after a CMB is to gather and distribute information to group members who requested it. Individual contacts are frequently necessary after a CMB. Follow-up includes making sure people who need referrals receive contact information to complete the referral process. New information should be gathered and plans made for the next CMB presentation if one is necessary.

Section Five
Interactive Group Crisis Intervention: Defusing

Something to think about:

"...hearing from peers may be more helpful than receiving guidance from a therapist since peers can identify with one another." - Irvin David Yalom, MD, 2005, Stanford University

The core elements of CISM covered in this section are in bold and enlarged letters below:

1. Assessment and Triage of people in crisis
2. Listening skills, The SAFER-R model, and individual crisis intervention.
3. Informational group processes.
4. **Interactive group processes.**
5. Strategic Planning, Incident assessment, Operations management, *Target, Types, Timing, Theme, and Team.*
6. Personal and Community resilience. (Resiliency includes the concepts of *resistance, resilience, and recovery.*)

** IMPORTANT INFORMATION **

Defusing: Introduction and Background

A defusing is an interactive group process conducted a short time after a homogeneous group has been exposed to a traumatic event. A homogeneous group is an essential requirement for the use of the defusing process. Usually, the **defusing is provided within an 8-hour time frame after the traumatic experience.** Occasionally, an extraordinarily powerful event may occur. This may necessitate an expansion of the time allowed before the defusing up to about 12 hours. In any case, the defusing will become ineffective if too much time has elapsed from the end of the traumatic exposure. If a delay beyond the usual 8 hours occurs (12 hours in an extremely horrific case like the murder of a child or a major disaster), it is best _not_ to do the defusing, but to immediately provide a short Crisis Management Briefing and plan for a Critical Incident Stress Debriefing (CISD) instead. Support should be focused on individuals until the CISD can be provided a few days later.

Most CISM teams use the interactive "defusing" group process fairly often and with good results. The International Critical Incident Stress Foundation (ICISF) strongly encourages the use of the defusing process when it is appropriate. Defusing has the distinct advantage of being applied very soon after the traumatic event when the group members' emotional guards are down and their needs are high. Groups in crisis are more open to help (the right kind of help at the right place and time). The defusing process, when carefully conducted by well-trained CISM team members at the most advantageous time, may help a traumatized group to reestablish their unit cohesion. A defusing may also help the group to return to the high level of performance that it demonstrated before the traumatic experience.

Good assessment skills on the part of CISM team members are essential. A defusing is an opportunity to observe the symptoms of distress and make some decisions as to whether or not a debriefing is going to be required. If the personnel appear to have unfinished business, very intense reactions to the traumatic situation, or suppressed reactions when a stronger reaction would be typical, these conditions suggest that a Critical Incident Stress Debriefing would be helpful. The CISD would ordinarily be offered several days after the defusing.

In some cases, a defusing will be held at just the right time and the need for a Critical Incident Stress Debriefing may dissipate. Although that is not one of the aims of a defusing, it can be an unexpected, but positive, side effect in some circumstances. On the other hand, there are many occasions when a Critical Incident Stress Debriefing (CISD) should follow a defusing a few days later. When a CISD is conducted after a defusing, it may be more powerful than it would have been without the benefit of the defusing.

Certain complex situations may cause a CISM team to select different interventions instead of the defusing. A line-of-duty death is one of those circumstances. Instead of providing a defusing, a 5-phase CISD is conducted. The 5-Phase CISD is an advanced technique which is taught in the Advanced Group Crisis Intervention course. It is mentioned here only for familiarization purposes. Proper training is required to use the technique appropriately. The 5-phase CISD eliminates the thought and symptoms phases and utilizes only the:

- introduction,
- facts,
- reaction,
- teaching
- summary phases.

The 5-phase CISD has only three applications. 1) On the day of the death in a line-of –duty death situation. 2) On the day of death in a suicide of a colleague situation and 3) anytime you are dealing with a group of children in the 6 to 12 year old age range. The five-phase CISD process is short in duration and not as intense as the full 7-phase CISD. A detailed explanation of the modified (five-phase) CISD is presented in the Advanced Group Crisis Intervention course from the International Critical Incident Stress Foundation (ICISF).

In the case of a disaster, emergency response personnel are _not_ given a defusing at the conclusion of their work at the disaster site. Instead they are given Rest, Information, and Transition Services (RITS). (See the segment on RITS in section four of this manual.) It is important that the CISM team _not_ provide both a defusing and a RITS to the same groups of emergency personnel.

A defusing is aimed at a homogeneous group that was exposed to the same traumatic event. If there are several different types of homogeneous groups who experience a traumatic event (police, fire, emergency medical services, etc.), it is best to provide a separate defusing for each of the homogeneous groups involved.

The defusing process was designed to facilitate a brief discussion of a traumatic event by the homogeneous group that experienced the trauma. It plays two primary roles. First, it helps to stabilize a traumatized group and restore unit cohesion and unit performance. Second, it is an assessment tool that helps the CISM team to determine what other services may be needed. The discussion is *absolutely not* intended to be an in-depth review of the situation nor a deep therapeutic conversation regarding the reactions of the participants. It is inappropriate to attempt to have people "relive" a traumatic event or to have the group participants delve into the deep existential meaning of the traumatic event. Remember, a defusing is a brief discussion of a traumatic event among the members of a homogeneous group. Avoid discussions that go into excessive details or try to dig deeply into the participants' psychological processes and be satisfied with a brief overview and a broad assessment of group and individual needs.

Trained CISM team members conduct defusing sessions. In the past, some untrained people have attempted to provide defusings. Participants in these sessions have reported that the leaders tried to go into too much depth and the sessions became uncomfortably long in duration. Most defusings are run by a team of two peer support personnel in about twenty minutes. On occasion, a CISM trained mental health professional or a chaplain or clergy person and one or two peers may lead a defusing.

Follow-up services are always necessary after a defusing. Follow-up may be offered in the form of individual support services by phone or in person. Other follow-up services include Critical Incident Stress Debriefing, family support, education, or referral to mental health professionals.

** IMPORTANT INFORMATION **

Principles of Group Support:

- **Heterogeneous (mixed) groups** are best managed by the <u>informational group interventions</u> such as the Rest, Information, and Transition Services (RITS) or the Crisis Management Briefing (CMB) (see section four).

- The *provision of information* and practical guidelines to assist people during the crisis is the main objective of informational group interventions.
- **Homogeneous (similar) groups** are best served by <u>Interactional group interventions</u> such as the defusing and the Critical Incident Stress Debriefing (CISD). Defusing is presented in this section (five) and the CISD process is contained in section seven.

*** CRITICAL INFORMATION ***

What is a Homogeneous Group?

- For a group to be homogeneous there are three conditions:
  1. The group members have a shared **history** with each other
  2. The group has worked together or shared experiences together over a considerable **time.**
  3. There is an existing **relationship** between the group members so that they are thought of as a unit.

The primary objective of an interactive group intervention is a discussion of a traumatic incident in which members of a homogeneous group assist each other in understanding and resolving a traumatic experience. In other words, the traumatic experience is *processed* by the group members. Processing an experience means the group members gain a better understanding of the experience and they can then find ways to put it in perspective in their lives. The group members may be able to <u>*let-it-go*</u> or "*park* it" in a place in their minds where it does not cause as much distress. In some case they might even learn something from the traumatic experience that they can apply in their personal or professional lives.

Types of Groups:

- There are three types of groups:
  1. Primary groups – very homogeneous (examples: work groups, some classes, teams, families, task oriented committees, military or emergency services units, etc.)
  2. Secondary groups – some familiarity but mostly heterogeneous in nature (examples: schools, associations, armies, organizations, etc.)
  3. Random groups – extremely heterogeneous (examples: shoppers in a mall, travelers on plane or train, crowds, the general audience of a theatre, etc.). Interactive groups like defusing and CISD are *never* provided to random groups.
- Defusing and CISD were designed specifically for use with primary, homogeneous groups and should never be used with heterogeneous groups.
- "...the most effective groups have a common identity and a sense of shared purpose...." (Paturel, 2012).
- Interactive group interventions are more efficient than Informational group intervention to "process" a traumatic experience because they incorporate a discussion of the traumatic experience, not just information.
- Interactive groups equalize the knowledge and information that exists within groups and
- Interactive group discussions enhance unit cohesion and restore unit performance. That is one of the primary objectives of interactive groups.
- "Only recently have we been able to demonstrate how the group influences individual group members" (Kivlighan, 2012)
- According to A. Paturel on Kivlighan, "...new research shows two leaders are better than one. Members of co-led groups experience greater benefits than those of individually led groups. That second set of eyes and ears makes a big difference when group leaders are trying to follow multiple interactions...."

- Two peer support personnel lead a defusing. A two- person peer team is most typical. Sometimes a Mental Health Professional and one or two peers _share_ the leadership in a defusing. One of the peers usually has the primary leadership role. Another configuration is to have one or two peers and a clergy person or chaplain _share_ the leadership in a defusing. Again one of the peers assumes the primary leadership role.
- Anyone selected to be part of a team to provide a defusing must be trained in Critical Incident Stress Management procedures.
- "Research is also shedding light on how, exactly, groups help people heal. One important factor is the ability to interact with peers. Numerous studies, including Kivlighan's 2012 work in _Group Dynamics,_ have found that peer interactions tap into many therapeutic factors." (Paturel, 2012).
- A. Paturel states (as cited in Brown, 2012), "In cases of abuse or trauma, groups provide social support, they improve social networks and they can reduce stigma, isolation and feelings of alienation among members."
- In fact, according to Stanford University's Irvin David Yalom, MD (2005) book, _The Theory and Practice of Group Psychology,_ "...hearing from peers may be more helpful than receiving guidance from a therapist since peers can identify with one another." (Paturel, 2012)
- Irvin D. Yalom (2012), identifies ten therapeutic factors in effective groups:
    1. **_Impart information_**
    2. **_Instill hope_**
    3. **_Altruistic_**
    4. **_Universal concepts_**
    5. **_Corrective recapitulation_**
    6. **_Use socializing techniques_**
    7. **_Initiate behaviors_**
    8. **_Interpersonal learning_**
    9. **_Group cohesiveness_**
    10. **_Catharsis_**

The Healing Factors in Groups:

- Group members **impart information** to each other and the group leaders impart information to the members of the group.
- Groups **instill hope.** As some members begin to improve, others realized they, too, are able to cope and recover.
- Group members are **altruistic** and will support one another during and after the group process.
- Groups reduce the **universal concepts** that a person is alone or unique.
- Group members must surrender a faulty idea ("It is all my fault"). Then they have to surrender again to a more appropriate idea ("We were all in this together."). This is called **Corrective Recapitulation.**
- Groups **use socializing techniques** in which members guide, encourage and correct each other.
- Group members frequently **initiate behaviors** by making suggestions to one another about what can be done to recover.
- Group members experience **interpersonal learning** by listening to each other and hearing how one or another of the group members is managing the distress of the trauma. This often motivates them to resume and improve unit performance.
- Groups that have experienced and discussed the same traumatic events frequently gain **group cohesiveness** by being united in their thinking and perceptions about the event.
- Homogeneous groups have developed trust by a shared history, spending time together, and by developing relationships with one another. The members typically assist each other in the process of **catharsis** – the expression of difficult, emotionally laden information.
- Detailed information on both informational and interactional group crisis interventions as well as the group dynamics that present in all groups can be found in the book: *Group Crisis Support: Why It Works, When And How To Provide It.*

Defusing

Definition: A shortened version of the Critical Incident Stress Debriefing (CISD) that is provided within hours of the traumatic event.

Providers: Routinely, two peer support personnel. The providers must always be trained in Critical Incident Stress Management (CISM) procedures.

Segments: 1. Introduction
2. Exploration
3. Information

Length of time: Between 20 and 45 minutes. (a typical defusing is 20-30 minutes in length)

Best Applied: Must be provided within 8 hours of a traumatic incident. Defusing is generally most effective when provided as close to the ending of the event as reasonable. Most occur within 2 hours of the event.

Target: Homogeneous groups only. Group size is usually small usually 2 – 20 people. Multiple defusing sessions for different groups of front-line workers (nurses, paramedics, police officers, firefighters, etc.) may be conducted for the same incident. Examples of usual target groups are engine companies, ambulance crews, emergency department staff, police squads, tactical units, and specialty teams.

Location of Defusing: A neutral environment free of distractions

Goals:

1. Mitigate the impact of the traumatic event.
2. Reduce cognitive, emotional and physiological symptoms.
3. Accelerate the recovery process
4. Assess the need for CISD and other services.
5. Identify any individuals who may need additional assistance.

Process:

1. Establish a non-threatening meeting environment.
2. Deliver some brief introductory remarks
3. Go over some basic guidelines for the defusing.
4. Ask the group members to give an overview or a thumbnail sketch of the traumatic incident.
5. Do not go around the room but let whoever wishes to say something to do so.
6. Gently invite anyone who has remained silent to add anything they wish to the discussion, but never pressure anyone to speak if they choose not to.
7. The defusing team's aim is to equalize the information among the group members. Most people experienced the traumatic event from different vantage points and it is often helpful for all of the group members to know what happened from other people's points of view.
8. Allow whatever emotional ventilation of trauma experience that group members wish to express.
9. One aim of defusing is to restore cognitive processing to the group members.
10. Do not probe for details. Just listen to and accept what the participants say.

11. Provide information on stress and symptom management as well as suggestions for recovery.
12. Affirm the value of the participants in the defusing.
13. Establish methods to arrange for additional support.
14. Develop positive outcome expectancies for the group members.

Contraindications:

1. Usually not applied to disasters, except as a part of a larger CISM program and only for small homogeneous groups that have experienced extremely stressful circumstances during the disaster operations.
2. Rest, Information, and Transition Services (RITS) for emergency personnel or Crisis Management Briefings for the citizens [see section four in this student manual for additional information] are often utilized for large-scale incidents and may be used instead of the defusing process.
3. Do not use the defusing with line-of-duty deaths. It is more helpful to use the 5-phase modified CISD process described in the CISM: Advanced Group Crisis Intervention course.
4. If RITS sessions are conducted during disaster operations, do _not_ also provide defusing processes. Providing both services to the same groups is _overkill_. The usual result is anger and frustration in the disaster workers.

Defusing Components:

1. Introduction
2. Exploration
3. Information

Introduction:	1. Introduce the team members presenting the defusing.
	2. State the purpose of the meeting (provide support to the group).
	3. Describe the process (a structured conversation regarding a traumatic event that the group members encountered together).
	4. State the goals of a defusing (reduction of acute distress, provision of helpful guidelines, restoration of unit cohesion and a return to unit performance).
	5. Motivate the participants
	6. Set the rules or guidelines for the defusing.
	7. Stress the point that all participants must respect the confidential nature of the defusing and _not_ discuss other participants' views, thoughts and feelings outside of the defusing.
	8. Reassure the participants that a defusing is neither psychotherapy nor a substitute for psychotherapy.
	9. State clearly that the defusing is not part of any type of an investigation.
	10. Ask the participants to complete the defusing process.
	11. Offer to provide individual support after the defusing session.
Exploration:	1. Ask the participants to provide a brief description of the traumatic event from their point of view of the event.
	2. Ask a few clarifying question as a natural part of the conversation.
	3. The participants share as much of their experience of the traumatic event and their reactions to it as they feel comfortable.
	4. The defusing team listens carefully, formulates new questions if necessary, and

observes the participants to determine if some of them will need individual support after the defusing concludes.

Information:

1. The defusing team reassures the participants that their reactions and the signals of distress they are encountering are normal, healthy responses of normal, healthy people to a terribly abnormal event.
2. The defusing team-teaches the participants that their normal reactions can be uncomfortable or even painful, but they will generally recede during the next few days to a week in most cases.
3. The defusing team presents suggestions that might help group participants recover from the traumatic experience.
4. Typical suggestions include issues such as nutrition, exercise, recreation, sleep, rest, communicating with loved ones, family life, staying active, returning to work responsibilities, and looking out for one's fellow workers.

Notes on defusing:

1. Once a CISM team is established and they provide a) more education presentations, b) more individual contacts with distressed personnel, and c) more defusing processes immediately after a traumatic event, the overall number of Critical Incident Stress Debriefings tends to go down. The reason is that the CISM teams are catching the distressed personnel earlier and intervening at the most advantageous times.
2. A well run defusing usually accomplishes one of two things:
   a) *It helps to restore unit cohesion and Unite performance.* In some cases the defusing may eliminate the need for a CISD. That

is not a goal of a defusing. Instead, it is a by-product of the defusing. That is, when it occurs, is an accidental positive effect of the defusing.

b) It helps to improve communications among the group members. In some cases, the defusing will improve the willingness of the participants to open-up and communicate more actively during the Critical Incident Stress Debriefing that is scheduled for a few days after the event.

The defusing reduces anxiety about discussing a traumatic event and the participants may understand that a discussion of one's experience of a traumatic event is helpful to themselves and to the other members of the group.

3. A defusing (3 parts) is less complex than the Critical Incident Stress Debriefing (7 steps).
4. No note taking is allowed in a defusing.
5. Do not go around the room.
6. People speak if they wish or remain silent if they wish.
7. The defusing is only useful for a few hours (typically 1 to 3 hours) after a traumatic event. The earlier it can be applied, the better the results. After 8 to 12 hours it is best not to use the defusing. By then, people are re-establishing their protective shields and their guards are up again. Getting them to talk in a group setting would be difficult at best. Instead, resort to individual consultations and set up a Critical Incident Stress Debriefing a few days later. Once they settle down a bit, they can speak in a group setting at the Critical Incident Stress Debriefing.

8. A defusing is conducted at a facility away from the scene – never at the scene.
9. The introductory remarks for a defusing vary somewhat from those of a Critical Incident Stress Debriefing. CISM team members should be very familiar with the differences.
10. The introductory remarks for a defusing can be found in section six. The introductory remarks for the Critical Incident Stress Debriefing can be found in section seven.

References

Kivlighan, D. M. (2012). Group dynamics: Theory, research and practice, *Monitor on Psychology,*

Mitchell, J. T. (2007). *Group crisis support: Why it works, when and how to provide it.* Ellicott City, MD: Chevron Publishing.

Paturel, A. (November 2012). Power in numbers. *Monitor on Psychology,* pp 48, 49

Yalom, I. D. (2005). *The theory and practice of group psychology,* New York, NY: Basic Books

Section Six
Practice Exercises for Defusing

Something to think about:

"For the things we have to learn before we can do them, we learn by doing them." — Aristotle, The Nicomachean Ethics

The core elements of CISM covered in this section are in bold and enlarged letters below:

1. Assessment and Triage of people in crisis
2. Listening skills, The SAFER-R model, and individual crisis intervention.
3. Informational group processes.
4. **Interactive group processes.**
5. Strategic Planning, Incident assessment, Operations management, *Target, Types, Timing, Theme, and Team*
6. Personal and Community resilience. (Resiliency includes the concepts of *resistance, resilience, and recovery.*)

** IMPORTANT INFORMATION **

This section   of the student manual covers practice exercises to enhance one's understanding of **defusing**. It focuses on experiential learning. The practice exercises and role-plays help participants to ultimately apply the defusing process in real situations in the future.

There are a few DVD's that demonstrate a defusing. It is very important that one of these DVD programs be shown in the training process so that participants can see how a defusing should be conducted.

Exercise One: Introductory Remarks for Defusing

Round One: Readers

Students will practice the introductory remarks for defusing in groups of four sitting in a circle. Two of them will alternate *reading* all the introductory remarks. The first one reads the first remark; the next one reads the second remark. Then the first reader presents the third remark and the second reader then reads the fourth remark and so on until all the remarks are read. The other two members of the exercise group will *listen* carefully while the readers go through a reading of all the remarks.

Round two: Paraphrasers

The two who were listening to the reading of the remarks during the first round now do something similar. Instead of reading the remarks, however, they will alternate going through the remarks one after another and *paraphrase* the remarks into their own words. The first will look at the first remark and immediately paraphrase it. The second will do the same for the second remark. Then the first paraphraser will present the third remark and the second paraphraser will handle the fourth remark until all of the remarks have been paraphrased.

NOTE: *In the practice session all remarks are read and paraphrased. In a real defusing,* however, that never takes place. Only selected remarks are made. The team of CISM peers or the combined team of mental health professionals, clergy and peers must choose from the list the remarks that are most applicable to the group needing the defusing. The most common remarks selected for presentation in a defusing are those that address issues such as confidentiality, the right to not speak if one chooses not to, and that the defusing is not investigative. Defusing team members can add items not on the list if necessary.

The Introductory Remarks for Defusing

These remarks will help a CISM team assigned to do a defusing to begin the process. It is not necessary to state each of the items below. The needs of the group and their experience with previous group crisis intervention techniques may help to guide the CISM team as they begin the defusing process. At times additional guidelines may need to be presented by the defusing team. Although it is okay to have the student manuals open when people are practicing the introductory remarks, manuals should *never* be open in real-life situations. CISM team members who are conducting a defusing should be very familiar with the introductory remarks and they should state them without having to resort to the manuals or to notes. Each team member should introduce him- or herself and then the necessary introductory remarks should be delivered to the participants in the defusing.

(Your own wording and personal style should be used when you are conducting a real defusing.)

- Hello, my name is _____ and I am a member of the _____ CISM team. My partner(s) in this defusing will introduce themselves now. We will work together to guide you through this brief conversation about the distressing event you just experienced.

- Each of you has a little different view of the event and we want you to feel comfortable discussing your own experience of the situation. Everyone's view counts. We are not here to criticize or critique the situation or your performance. So, we are asking that you do not criticize your colleagues. If things happened during the operations that need to be corrected, they can be addressed in a different process than this one.

- Our team is not part of any investigative procedure. No reports of our discussion here will be made. Things that you tell us are not repeated outside of this group. The only information given to supervisors or administrators relates only to suggestions for things they might do to help your group.

- We simply want to give everyone an opportunity to say what each person believes is important about the situation. Then we will give you some useful information and guidelines to help you recover from this experience.

- No one has to talk although we encourage your active participation because something you might say could be helpful to others in your group.

- There is no specific order to this defusing discussion. We do _not_ go around the room. If you wish to add something to the discussion, just speak up when you wish to do so. We would just ask that, out of courtesy, you allow someone, who is already speaking, to finish his or her comment before you begin speaking.

- We know that sometimes in situations like the one you just went through operational procedures are not always perfect. We are not here to judge problems and mistakes. They happen. We are more interested in how you are doing as a human being who went through a difficult or distressing experience.

- We do not need excessive details about the event. A broad, thumbnail sketch of the situation would be most helpful at this time. Our intention is to have a positive, helpful discussion that provides good information and ultimately benefits each of you.

- In many defusing processes, we have found that one comment sometimes can clarify the experience for other participants in the group.

- This meeting is about enhancing your unit's cohesion. It is also helpful in restoring your group to its normal level of performance.

- Talking about the experience often puts things in perspective and that helps to restore the group members to normal work functions.

Many times people learn something in these group defusings that helps them in future experiences.

- Our team holds what you say in this defusing in confidence. We ask that each of you commit yourself to do the same. Please do not discuss other people's reactions outside of this session. Every member of this defusing should respect the right to privacy that everyone in the group has. Trust is important and we need everyone to trust that what they say will not be discussed outside of this group. You may speak about your reactions to the incident as much as you choose, but please do not discuss other people's reactions to the traumatic event. No note taking is permitted.

- A defusing is a _guided conversation_. It is not psychotherapy nor is it a substitute for psychotherapy.

- The defusing process will not take very long. Typically, these meetings take about 20 to 30 minutes. We are not in a rush, however, so take as much time as you need to discuss the event.

- Our team will be here for a while once the defusing ends. Feel free to approach us if you would like to talk to us outside of the group.

- If we need to get together again later, we are certainly willing to do that. If needed, there are several other support services that can help take the edge off this event.

- It will help our team to provide you with the most useful information toward the end of this meeting if you can give us an overview of what you went through during the incident.

- We do not need a lot of detail, but we may ask a few questions so we are clear about the main aspects of the situation.

- Sometimes it helps to know who got involved first and who came in next.

- If someone can give us a thumbnail sketch of the situation we would appreciate it.

- Since we are not going around the room we will need someone to start.

- Okay, let's begin. Can someone please give us a brief overview of the situation and tell us what happened.

Exercise Two: Defusing Practice

The course instructor will divide the course attendees into groups of eight by combining two groups of four together after the Introductory Remarks for Defusing exercise. The groups of eight will participate in a defusing exercise based on a scenario presented by the instructor. Two members of the group will act as CISM trained peer support personnel. Five will play the role of a homogeneous group that has experienced a significant traumatic event and is in need of a defusing. The sixth will function as an observer and use the "Observing a Defusing" form that follows.

OBSERVING A DEFUSING

1. The defusing has three (3) separate stages. As you observe the defusing, write a brief summary of what you saw happening within each of the defusing stages.

Introduction –

Exploration –

Information –

2. What was the role of the leader in each of the defusing stages?

3. What outcome was achieved by the end of the defusing?

Section Seven
Interactive Group Crisis Intervention:
Critical Incident Stress Debriefing (CISD)

Something to think about:

"...whatever life throws at us, our individual responses will be all the stronger for working together and sharing the load."
- Queen Elizabeth II

The core elements of CISM covered in this section are in bold and enlarged letters below:

1.   Assessment and Triage of people in crisis
2.   Listening skills, The SAFER-R model, and individual crisis intervention.
3.   Informational group processes.
4.   **Interactive group processes**.
5.   Strategic   Planning,   Incident   assessment,   Operations management, Target, Types, Timing, Theme, and Team
6.   Personal and Community resilience. (Resiliency includes the concepts of resistance, resilience, and recovery.)

The Word "Debriefing"

The word *debriefing* has numerous meanings. It may mean a feedback session or an interview, a probe, or an examination of a situation. It some cases, it means a questioning or fact gathering session after an event. Sometimes it means a process by which an explanation of an experience is gained. Everyone, therefore, should be cautious when using the word debriefing by itself. The word, when used alone, may imply too many dissimilar things to different people. By itself, the word *debriefing* does **_not_** at all accurately portray the real meaning of the interactive group process known as "Critical Incident Stress Debriefing."

Critical Incident Stress Debriefing

The author of this student manual, Dr. Jeffrey T. Mitchell of the University of Maryland Baltimore County, developed the interactive group process called Critical Incident Stress Debriefing (CISD) beginning in 1974. The first publication on CISD appeared in 1983 in the *Journal of Emergency Medical Services*. Even in that first article, many types of interventions were presented as part of a broad, systematic approach to managing distress in emergency personnel.

The Critical Incident Stress Debriefing was developed solely as a *support service* for <u>*homogeneous groups*</u> who had experienced a traumatic event. The word "support" means: *to help keep a person or a group stable; to care for people, to sustain them, or to reinforce the individual or the group.* Other meanings for the word support are: *to give active help and encouragement; to help in a crisis; to provide active assistance; to provide comfort; or to bear some of the weight.* The word support best describes what CISM teams do when they provide a CISD.

CISD is not psychotherapy nor is it a substitute for psychotherapy. It was never intended to be a therapy process or to be used as a cure for any physical or mental problem or disorder.

The CISD process is part of a broad package of crisis intervention tactics, Critical Incident Stress Management (CISM), and **it should never be used in isolation from other interventions**. Stress management education, for instance, is desirable long before personnel are traumatized by a specific incident. Every effort should be made to build up individual and group resistance and resilience. At the very least, follow-up is always required whenever a CISD is provided. For a number of reasons, the CISD process has received a great deal of unnecessary attention during the last decade. Some of that undue attention may have generated misinformation and faulty applications of the model. The material in this student manual will provide accurate information on the CISD process and guide appropriately trained providers in properly applying the process with traumatized and stressed homogeneous groups.

A Critical Incident Stress Debriefing (CISD) is an interactive *group support process* designed specifically for application with small, homogeneous (primary) groups that have experienced roughly the same level of exposure to the same traumatic event. It is a group crisis intervention procedure. Although it has been used successfully with a wide range of homogeneous populations, such as school children, businesses and industries, it should be kept in mind that it was originally developed for operational groups such as firefighters, flight crews, police officers, emergency medical crews, and military personnel who know each other and who share both a common history and positive relationships with one another. *It is <u>inappropriate</u> to use the CISD group crisis intervention process with groups that are heterogeneous. Likewise, it is <u>inappropriate</u> to use the CISD model with individuals.* The CISD process was never designed for individual primary victims such as those who are ill, injured, medicated, psychotic, or who are hospital patients, victims of violence, suicidal ideation, or people currently undergoing grave personal threat. It is an *<u>egregious (outrageous or flagrant) violation</u>* of the standard principles and practices of CISD to apply this group crisis intervention process to individual women who had difficult pregnancies, complicated deliveries, miscarriages, or stillborn babies. It is also an *<u>egregious violation</u>* of the standards of practice to apply the CISD interactive group crisis intervention process to individual auto accident victims, sexual assault victims, burn victims and dog bite victims. These misguided and horribly flawed applications of the CISD group crisis intervention model are unequivocally condemned. **CISD should <u>only</u> be used with appropriate <u>*homogeneous*</u> groups.**

Homogeneous Groups
Three conditions are necessary for a group to be a homogeneous group.
   1) There must be ***existing relationships among the group members*** before the traumatic event occurred.

2) There must be a **shared history**. That shared history includes the fact that the group members experienced the same traumatic experience.
3) Sufficient **time together** should have elapsed so that the **group members are thought of as if one**.

Goals of CISD

The main goals of a CISD are to support the *primary group* after a shared traumatic experience and to restore the unit's cohesion and performance. In no way should the supportive CISD small group process be construed to be psychotherapy or a substitute for psychotherapy. The CISD is a not a treatment or a cure for any form of mental disorder, including Posttraumatic Stress Disorder (PTSD). *Any possible preventative value against PTSD would be of a secondary nature, not primary.* The prevention of PTSD is <u>not</u> listed as one of the primary goals of the CISD process. The actual goals of the CISD process are:
1) *Mitigation of the crisis response,*
2) Assist in the *restoration of the group's ability to function* and
3) *Identification of individuals within the small homogeneous group who might need additional support or a referral* for professional care.

The CISD interactive crisis intervention group process, therefore, plays a far greater screening and referral role than psychotherapeutic role.

<u>CISD is not a stand-a-lone process</u>.

Although it is an important process for stressed homogeneous groups, the <u>*CISD is not a stand-a-lone process*</u>. It should always be used as only one component of a comprehensive program that includes at least assessment, individual support, and follow-up services. The CISD interactive group crisis support process is only one element of the larger, comprehensive, integrative, systematic and multi-component CISM program.

Benefits of CISD

There are many benefits of the interactive group CISD process. It provides:
1) Practical information that serves as a useful guide for the group members' recovery from a traumatic experience.

2) A CISD may also help the group members understand that they are not alone in the trauma experience.

3) Help is available if they want it. It is generally reassuring to the members of the group to know that they are not unique and that others may be experiencing the same physical and emotional effects.

4) The CISD aims at normalizing the reactions that the group members are experiencing after the critical incident.

NOTE: The benefits of the CISD can only be realized when the interactive group process is conducted by trained personnel. Reading this book without practical training is insufficient to achieve a proper level of skill to provide the CISD process.

The Stages of a CISD

There are seven steps or stages in the interactive group CISD process. They are presented here to round out this brief discussion on CISD as a component of a larger, more comprehensive program. More detailed information will be added later in this section of the student manual.

1) *Brief introduction* by the crisis team members
2) *Brief situation review* or a Facts phase
3) First *impressions* or Thought phase of the traumatic event
4) Aspects of the event that produced the *greatest personnel impact on you or Reactions phase*
5) *Signals of distress*
6) *Stress information and guidelines for recovery* or Teaching phase
7) *Summary* or Re-entry phase

The preponderance of the studies cited in the literature on CISD indicate a positive effect if two conditions are in place. The **first** is that **people who conduct the interactive group CISD process are properly trained to do so.** The **second** condition is that **the providers of the service must adhere to the standard of practice** for the CISD homogeneous group support process that have been established and promulgated since 1983.

Crucial Elements of CISD

- A structured homogeneous group discussion of a traumatic event.
- Requires a team approach.
- Minimal team is 2 people. One is a CISM trained mental health professional the other is a peer support person.
- Typical team is 3 CISM trained people. One is a mental health professional, the other two are peer support personnel.
- A CISM trained clergy person or chaplain may be added to the team providing the CISD.
- Peer support personnel are essential for emergency and military personnel as well as for transportation workers, hospital employees and some industries.
- Peer support may not be necessary when dealing with certain businesses and industries or in organizations where there is little evidence of a unique subculture and only limited amounts of group cohesiveness and bonding.
- CISD may be provided to *only homogeneous groups*.
- Typical group sizes may range from 2 to 20. Somewhat larger groups may occur under some circumstances. CISM team members must do a strategic assessment and develop a crisis action plan that makes sense in light of the circumstances and the composition of the homogeneous group.
- Most CISD's last between one and three hours depending on the size of the group and the intensity of the traumatic experience encountered by the group. *No breaks are taken*.
- If a participant leaves the CISD, one of the team members will follow that person out of the room. If it is a "personal needs break" only, the CISM team member will wait for the person and talk with that person for a few minutes to make sure he or she is okay. Then the CISM team member will encourage the person to return to the room. If the person needs individual support the CISM team member may stay with the person as long as necessary. Efforts should be made to get the person to return to the group as soon as they are ready.

- With emergency personnel and military personnel, _defusing and individual support services_ are provided during the first 8-12 hours after the incident. **The CISD is generally held off for at least 24 hours to give operations personnel the time to calm their systems down a little and get off the "operations mode." Most CISD's are conducted between 24-72 hours after the event.** If circumstances warrant it, they may be a few days later. When the CISD is complete, follow-up is required.
- CISM teams are cautioned not to let too long a time pass before providing the CISD. The process loses most of its power to help if too much time passes before the service is provided.
- Disasters, however, are complex and psychologically intense, and therefore, CISDs may need to be delayed for weeks until operations personnel complete search and rescue and other functions at the scene.
- CISM teams must engage in careful planning to determine the best time to deliver the CISD services.
- Consider the 5-T strategic planning formula when developing the plan for support services:
  a. **Target** (s) – who needs assistance, who may not need assistance?
  b. **Type** (s) – what types of assistance will the targets need?
  c. **Timing** – when is the best time to deliver the services?
  d. **Theme** – What are the threats involved at the incident. What are the concerns, considerations, complications and questions that may influence everything the CISM team does?
  e. **Team** – Who are the best team members to be deployed on this specific incident?
- Citizen populations, which may not share the same level of esprit-de-corps as emergency and military personnel, may be ready for the CISD earlier. It is not unusual to provide a CISD on the same day as the event for citizens. They do not have operational duties and they may be quite distressed by the incident. We should try to provide services when people are ready for help and we should not rely on some arbitrary formula to determine the best time for providing assistance. **IMPORTANT REMINDER:** even with citizens the group must be homogeneous, **not** heterogeneous.

- What people tell CISM team members during a CISD should be treated with a high degree of confidentiality. What is said in a CISD should not be disclosed to others.
- There should be a ratio of one CISM team member for every 5 to 7 participants in a CISD.
- A CISD may be conducted around a conference table or in an open circle if there are too many people for a conference table.

Room Arrangements for CISD

Two-person team

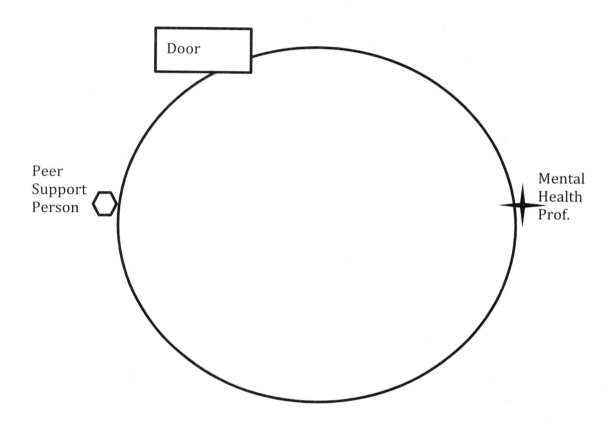

Note: The nearly perfect circles shown in these diagrams are only used to describe concepts. In reality, we never achieve a perfect circle. Most times the circles are more like ovals, rectangles, or squares. The idea is to have the participants facing each other as we would in a normal conversation. You may have a conference table around which everyone is gathered or, if the group size is small, a coffee table would be find. Try to make people comfortable and do not get caught-up in trying to create unnatural circles.

Room Arrangement for CISD
Three-person team

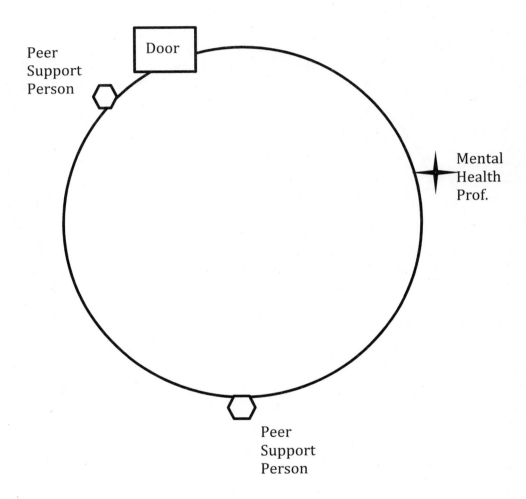

Room Arrangement for CISD

Four-person team

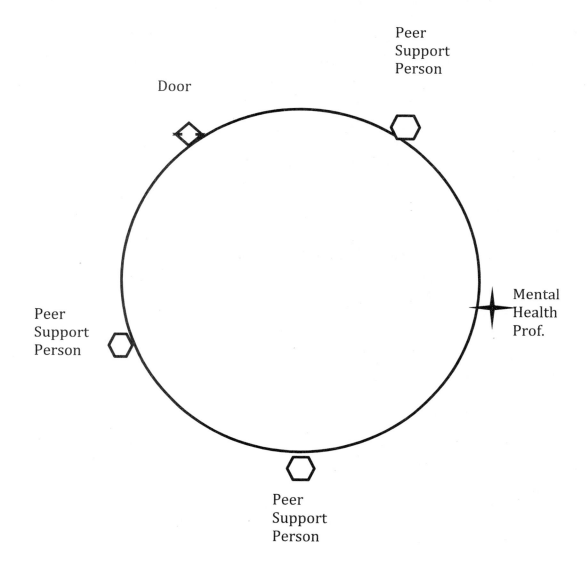

Peer
Support
Person

Door

Peer
Support
Person

Mental
Health
Prof.

Peer
Support
Person

Room Arrangement for CISD
Note: Participant spread may not always be equal in all areas of the circle. Space the team members out as suggested in the graphic below. Participants will fill in between the CISM team members. Do not worry if the participants are not equally distributed in the available space.

Four-person team (participants spread between them)

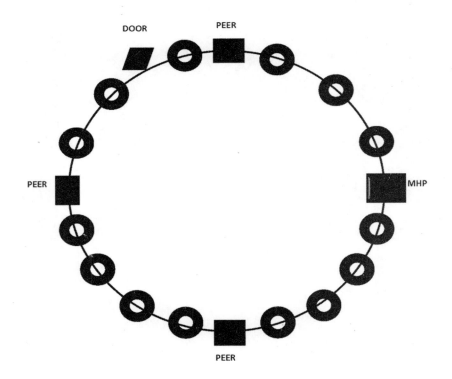

CISD Diagram

In the CISD diagram, items listed toward the top of the illustration are closer to the cognitive (intellectual) domain. Those items toward the bottom are closer to the affective (emotional) domain.

Phases of a CISD

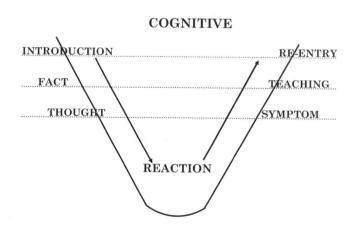

*** CRITICAL INFORMATION ***

Procedural Issues: Unlike the defusing in which we do *not* go around the room, but just allow people who desire to speak to do so when they wish, <u>in the CISD</u> we *do* go around the room <u>twice</u> to offer everyone the opportunity to say something if they wish. The first time is in the fact phase and the second go around is in the thought phase. After those two phases, we no longer go around the room and, instead, we allow people to speak when they wish. If people do not wish to take the opportunity to say something in the group all they need to do is say "pass" or wave a hand that indicates we should just move onto the next person. No one ever has to speak in a CISD if he or she does not wish to speak.

<u>*Line-of-Duty deaths and suicide of a colleague*</u>. There is another procedural guideline that refers only to cases involving a suicide of a colleague or the line of duty death. In those two cases we would never go around the room and have each person speak in the CISD. The emotions in those two events are so intense that going around the room would exert excessive pressure on the group participants. It is better just to allow people to speak only if and when they wish to do so in the CISD.

Additional training for group crisis intervention is recommended for any CISM team members who might someday have to deal with a suicide of a colleague or a line of duty death. The International Critical Incident Stress Foundation (ICISF) offers Advanced Group Crisis Intervention courses and these are highly recommended. They are enormously helpful when a CISM team has to deal with complex situations such as suicide of a colleague, line of duty deaths, significantly delayed group interventions, multiple-incident CISDs, and group interventions related to a major disaster.

Descriptions and Prompts for Each Stage of the CISD

Introduction: Introduce the CISM team members. Lower group anxiety. Go over some simple, common ground rules. Motivate the participants.

Common ground rules for the CISD
   a) Everyone is welcome to speak in the CISD, but <u>no one is required to speak</u> if they choose not to.
   b) Whatever is said must be held in confidence. The CISM team members abide by this guideline and all participants should be committed to do so as well.
   c) No reports will be given to supervisors, commanders or administrators. The only information shared with supervisors, command officers, and administrators is some suggestions on how to assist their personnel through the stress generated by the traumatic event.
   d) No notes or recordings are allowed during the CISD.
   e) No breaks are taken during the CISD, but if personal needs must be taken care of, we would ask the individual to leave the room quietly and return as quickly as possible. Our team policy is that we always send one of our peer support personnel out to check on the welfare of any person who has left the CISD.
   f) A CISD is not an operations critique. It focuses more on the human elements of the experience than it does on the operational procedures.
   g) The CISD is not psychotherapy or a substitute for psychology. Neither is it an investigative tool. It is all about support, reestablishing unit cohesion, and restoring unit performance.

Fact
The fact phase gives the participants the opportunity to briefly describe the event they experienced. Details are not necessary. There is no "reliving" of the event. Just enough information is shared to provide the CISM team members who are conducting the CISD with a broad overview of what happened during the incident. Typical prompts are "Please tell us your name and briefly describe what happened during the incident from your perspective. We just need a broad overview or a thumbnail sketch of the incident. Your remarks will help our team

provide you with the most helpful information later in this Critical Incident Stress Debriefing."

Sometimes a larger than expected group shows up at the CISD. When the group size gets beyond 25, an alternative form of questioning may be employed. Instead of going around the room and inviting every person to speak if they wish, the CISM team can ask, "Who got involved in this event first? Can you tell us briefly what happened? Who came next? What happened from your point of view? Who arrived next and what happened then? Anyone else who would like to add anything to what has been said so far?" After 5 or 6 people speak, enough information about the incident will have been stated by the group members and the team can move on to the next stage of the CISD. This random information gathering process is much less time consuming than going around the room and having each person speak.

Thought
The thought phase of the CISD is a transitional phase from the cognitive domain to the affective domain. It is easier for people to discuss the facts of a situation first before they discuss the emotional aspects of the situation. The thought phase allows for a smooth transition because some facts are still presented, but the group members may also present thoughts and impressions with somewhat more emotional content. The prompts for the thought phase are fairly open-ended and do not restrict one's answers to the cognitive domain alone.

The prompts in the thought phase are usually: "What was your first or most prominent thought during the incident?" Did you experience any disquieting or unusual thoughts while you were engaged in the incident?

Remember, you may invite everyone to discuss the event, but no one is ever required to speak in a CISD.

Reaction
The reaction phase of the CISD may contain the most emotional content. That does not mean that people cry and get visibly emotionally distressed. Some may, but the most important thing is not so much an open display of emotions, but a frank discussion of the experience.

The usual prompts in the reaction phase are: "What was the worst part of the event for you personally?" or "If you could magically go back to the scene and erase one part, with the outcome being the same, what one part would you most want to erase?" or "Is there any aspect of the event that caused you the most pain and personal distress?"

Symptoms

In the CISD, the symptoms phase offers the opportunity for the participants to briefly discuss the cognitive, physical, emotional, and behavioral symptoms that arose in the aftermath of a traumatic event. The main purpose of this discussion is to confirm that the symptoms discussed are common and normal reactions to a traumatic event.

The usual prompts used in the symptoms Phase are the following: "What kinds of symptoms have you been encountering since the incident?" or "What has life been like for you since the event?" or "What signals of distress have you noticed in yourself since this happened?"

Teaching

One of the most important phases in the CISD is the teaching phase. The CISM team can explain and normalize the symptoms discussed in the previous phase and which might have arisen in other phases of the CISD. In this phase the CISM team will provide stress management information and guidelines for recovery. In certain circumstances, if it would benefit the participants, the CISM may inform the group if there are other resources that might be helpful.

Re-entry or Summary

The re-entry phase of the CISD serves as an opportunity to answer any questions that have not yet been addressed. The re-entry phase is also the time when issues that have not previously been discussed in the CISD may come up. The CISD should not come to a close until the majority of the group has returned to the cognitive domain. Finally, the re-entry is the period when summaries are made final directions and guidance is presented. The CISM team will say its goodbyes and final comments as the CISD draws to a close.

Immediate Follow-up

As soon as the CISD ends, the CISM team members come to their feet and they begin to check on individuals to see how they are doing. The CISM team members shake hands with the participants. Every participant should have shaken hands, or made some type of contact, with at least one CISM team member. The CISM team may have targeted some participants during the CISD and they now begin individual contacts to assure maximal recovery of the personnel.

NOTES:

1) In 2007, the titles of the seven phases or segments of the CISD were reworded and clarified to assist the United Nations as well as CISM teams around the world.

2) The prompts presented in the previous segments of this section are the most frequently used. CISM team members should paraphrase those prompts into their own words. That will make them sound realistic and sincere and not contrived. Similar questions can be asked with alternative wording that addresses the same themes as the prompts described above.

3) See the next paragraphs for some examples of the alternative or clarified CISD phase titles and prompts.

*** CRITICAL INFORMATION ***

Traditional Phase Titles	Clarified Phase Titles
1. Introduction	1. *Introduction*
2. Facts	2. *Brief situation review*
3. Thoughts	3. *First impressions of the event*
4. Reactions	4. *Aspect causing most personal distress*
5. Symptoms	5. *Signals of distress*
6. Teaching	6. *Stress management information and recovery guidelines*
7. Re-entry	7. *Summary*

Alternative Prompts

1. Introduction	Same as traditional introduction.
2. Brief situation review	Please give us a brief description of what happened. A broad picture or a thumbnail sketch of the experience would be helpful. Excessive details are not necessary.
3. First impressions	What were your first impressions of the incident? This might include thoughts or feelings like anxiety or fear or concern for your safety.
4. Aspect of the event causing the greatest personal distress.	"What caused you the most discomfort or distress while you were working on the situation?"
5. Signals of distress	"Our bodies and minds react to the things we experience. They sometimes signal us that we are distressed by what we see, hear, smell, taste, and feel or by the way our minds interpret the experience. What signals of distress showed up in you during and after this incident?
6. Stress management information and recovery guidelines	The CISM team conducting the CISD explains and normalizes the stress reactions in the participants and suggests guidelines for things that may help to reduce the participants stress reactions. Practical guidelines to recover from stress are a primary aim of this presentation.

7. Summary

Answer questions. Discuss any additional topics. Summarize the CISD and encourage unit cohesion and a return to individual and unit performance.

INTRODUCTORY REMARKS FOR CISD

A CISM team may introduce a Critical Incident Stress Debriefing (CISD) with the following remarks. They are somewhat different than those used for a defusing (see section five of this manual). One example of a difference between the defusing and the CISD is that *in a defusing* the CISM team members do <u>not</u> go around the room in order to offer everyone the opportunity to speak and *in the CISD* they <u>do</u> go around the room two different times.

It is not necessary to state each introductory item in each CISD. Some groups will not need all of the information contained in these remarks. These general remarks cover the main introductory points for the CISD. CISM team members should select the items from the introductory remarks list that they think are most suitable for the group they are working with in the CISD.

It is best that the concepts presented in this outline be given to a group in the words of the team members. They should <u>not</u> be read to the group from these pages. At times, it may be necessary to add additional comments not shown here. This can be done at the discretion of the team. The order of the presentation of the items is not of major importance. What is important is that the CISM team that is conducting the CISD should present the most important items for the good of the group. The asterisked items are essential. (* = core items).

- Team leader identifies self. Then each team member introduces him or herself. *
- We are here because of (describes or name the critical incident). *
- Some of you do not want to be here. You feel you don't need a CISD. Please remember even if you don't need help, others present here may. Please stay. You may be able to help some of the people in this room simply by your presence. This is more about your group's needs than it is about you. Please try to help clarify this event for the benefit of your group.
- Sometimes, one sentence you might share could make a positive difference for someone who is having difficulty with some aspect of the event. Please try to be helpful to one another.
- This is not a therapy process. It is much more about restoring the cohesion and the performance level of your unit. *

- These sessions often help to enhance a group's resilience, that is, the ability of the group to "bounce back" from a bad event.
- Some of you feel you can handle this on your own. That is probably true. However, experience demonstrates that people who try to handle everything alone take longer to do it. *
- A critical incident is any event that is extraordinary and produces significant reactions in emergency personnel. (Don't refer to emergency personnel if you are working with a homogeneous group of people who are not involved in emergency services.) The critical incident is so unusual that it overwhelms the usual, normal abilities emergency personnel have developed to cope with a situation.
- The CISD process is designed to lessen the overall impact of an event and to accelerate recovery in normal people who are having normal reactions to abnormal events. *
- We have found that people who talk about a bad incident eat better, sleep better, remain healthier, stay on the job longer, and do not have as much disruption in their home lives.
- The CISD process is a discussion of an unusual event but it is _not_ a critique or part of an investigation. *
- A CISD is not psychotherapy nor is it a substitute for psychotherapy. It is only a group support process.
- No notes are allowed. Neither do we allow recordings of what is said nor are the representatives of the media ever allowed.
- Everything that is said in this room is confidential. **(Heavily emphasize confidentiality).** _Nothing that another person says, except for what our team teaches you, should leave this room_. *
- You will be asked to speak two times in the CISD. The first time we ask each of you to tell us who you are, what your role was at the incident, and what happened during the incident. In the second question we will ask if you could cite your first thought once you stopped functioning on _automatic pilot_.
- You do not have to speak at any time if you do not wish to. However, we do _not_ recommend that because sometimes not speaking can do more harm than good. We recommend, instead, that you talk about the incident. *
- Remember, the people in this group are members of your unit. The CISD is more about something you do or say that can help someone else on your team than it is about you.

- Our main job is to get you back to your normal work and life activities and keep you as healthy and satisfied as possible. We are not here to take you out of service. We are here to listen to you and to help as best as we can. *

- You may ask any questions you wish and we'll try to help you out with some practical and useful information. Please ask any question anytime you wish.

- Please speak only for yourself. You cannot possibly speak adequately for how someone else is reacting. *

- Remember, confidentiality is the key. We need to have a pact of trust between all of us. Everyone has already been hurt enough by this event. Don't use anything you learn or hear in this room except information the team teaches you about stress management and recovery from a traumatic experience. *

- We do not want anyone to make judgment about anyone else. Every person has his own perspective. Let each state it without judgment. *

- We will not take any breaks. If you have to take care of your personal needs during the debriefing do so quietly and then return to this room as soon as possible. Leaving and not returning to this session may be harmful to you. Much of what we discuss at the end of the session is extremely valuable information that may be helpful. We don't want you to miss it so please hang in there with us. *

- Our team does not know all of you, so please do us a favor and look around the room and point out anyone who you think does not belong in this room. The CISM team members will briefly raise their hands so that you might more easily identify them. Anyone else who you don't recognize please point out and we will ask why the person is here. If an officer was at the scene he or she belongs here. In the case of line of duty death, the entire department may belong in one of these sessions.

- We would ask that the courtesies afforded to rank remain in effect, but we do not focus on a person's rank in these sessions. We are more concerned about how each person in this group is doing as a human being. Therefore a person's rank should not get in the way of participation in this discussion.

- Our greatest focus in these sessions is on your group's cohesiveness and a return to healthy performance.

- We will be around at the end of the session. If you want to talk to us, feel free. We are here for you. Anything you can't tell us in the group you are welcome to tell us alone. *
- We will begin in just a moment by asking you to tell us briefly about the incident.
- We would appreciate your turning off your pagers, cell phones and radios to help avoid distractions.
- One final reminder about *confidentiality* before we get into the facts of the situation. Let's keep whatever is heard here in this room confidential. *
- We'll have a handout or two at the end of the session.
- The next phase of the CISD, the fact phase, is now ready to begin.

NOTE: Detailed procedures for all of the phases of the CISD process can be found in the book, *Group Crisis Support* (Mitchell, 2007).

Critical Incident Stress Debriefing (CISD)

Definition: *The Critical Incident Stress Debriefing (CISD) is a structured, interactive group crisis intervention process for homogeneous groups only.* It is an <u>active, temporary, and supportive group crisis intervention</u> process that focuses on building up a group's resistance to traumatic stressors. The CISD also focuses on the group's resilience (the ability of a group to bounce back from a traumatic exposure). Finally, the CISD emphasizes unit cohesion and unit performance and the ability of the group to recover from a traumatic event and to resume its normal functions.

What CISD is _Not_: CISD is **_not_** any form of:

1. Psychotherapy
2. A substitute for psychotherapy
3. Professional counseling
4. A treatment for PTSD or any mental or physical disease or disorder
5. A cure for PTSD or any mental or physical disease or disorder

An organizational problem-solving process for administrative problems

Target: Small, homogeneous groups who have experienced the same traumatic event.

Application Criteria:
1. Small, **homogeneous group** (e.g. police officers in the same unit, a company of firefighters, a tactical squad, an emergency medical services crew, or a military squad, platoon or unit.)
2. The small group has **completed its mission** or the event has moved beyond the acute phases.

3. The members of the small group have encountered **about the same level of traumatic exposure** to the traumatic event

Goals:

1. Lower tension and mitigate a small group's reaction to a traumatic event.
2. Facilitation of normal recovery processes of normal people within a small group who are having normal reactions to an abnormal event.
3. Identification of people within a group who might be in need of additional individual support or, in some cases, a referral for professional psychotherapy.

Best Applied:

The Critical Incident Stress Debriefing (CISD) is ordinarily provided between 24 and 72 hours after a traumatic event. In some situations, such as a disaster in which people have continuous exposures to many disaster related event over time, a CISD may not be provided until several weeks have passed. Providers must consider the issue of psychological readiness for assistance. No help, no matter how skilled is really useful if it is provided at the wrong time.

Length of time:

A CISD may last between 1 and 3 hours depending on two primary factors:

1. The number of people in the group. (Obviously larger groups will take longer to discuss a traumatic event than smaller groups because there are more people who might wish to express their thoughts.)

2. The intensity of the traumatic event. (More intense events tend to generate stronger emotional reactions in the group members and those reactions are harder to express.)

Providers: Only people who are properly trained in CISM and specifically in the small group process of the CISD should provide the service to traumatized groups. Untrained providers present a serious threat.

Research in the field indicates that the greatest problems in crisis intervention arise when
1. People are untrained to provide the services or
2. When they violate standard procedures.

Facilitator Roles: *Mental Health Professional.*
Participates with the other CISM team members in the provision introductory remarks Monitors symptoms and signals of distress.
Keeps the process from turning into psychotherapy.
Assists in the teaching and summary phases.
Assists in providing referrals if necessary

Peer Support Personnel.
The peers co-facilitate the CISD with the mental health professional. One peer is assigned to monitor the door and keep out media and other unwanted people. If someone leaves the peer goes out and communicates with the person and attempts to have the person return to the CISD.
Peers engage in co-teaching the guidelines for stress recovery and the summary remarks.
Peers are very actin in connecting with the group participants after the CISD ends. They assist in providing referrals if any are necessary.
Peers are active in follow up with the participants. They usually being face-to-face and telephone contacts with a few days of the CISD. Sometimes peers arrange for a follow-up group meeting is such a service appears necessary.

Location: Neutral environments that are free of distractions are the best location for a CISD. They should be reasonably comfortable. The location should afford privacy and be accessible.

Process: There are seven steps to a Critical Incident Stress Debriefing (CISD). They are:

Traditional Prompts	*Alternative Prompts*
Introduction	Introduction
Fact	Brief situation review
Thought	First impression
Reaction	Most distressing part
Symptoms	Signals of distress
Teaching	Recovery guidelines
Re-entry	Summary

Sample Prompts: (see alternative prompts above)

Introduction   The CISM team members providing the CISD process spends about five minutes describing the process and laying out the basic guidelines. (The guidelines are presented in the Introductory Remarks for the CISD of this student manual.)

Fact   "It would help if you could give us a very brief overview of what happened during the incident. We will start off over here on my left and go around the circle. Anyone who does not wish to speak may 'pass' and we will go right on to the next person. Going around the room gives everyone the opportunity to speak if they wish. We do not need elaborate details. Just a few lines that tell us who you are, what your job was during the event and a brief thumbnail overview of the situation will be enough."

Thought   "What was your first or most prominent thought while you were going through the experience? Some people may have more personal thoughts and others might have had some strange thoughts. Whatever went through your mind is okay. So, your first thought when you realized you were actually thinking and not just functioning on an automatic mode? By the way, this is the last time we will go around the entire circle. After this if you want to join the discussion you can make a comment at any time."

Reactions   "What was the very worst thing about this event for you personally? Another way to phrase that question is to ask if you could go back to the situation and magically erase one aspect of the experience, even if the outcome was the same, what one piece would you most want to erase?"

| Symptoms | "What signals of distress did you pick up in yourself either while the situation was going on or in the few days that have passed since it ended? In other words how did your mind, your emotions, your body or behaviors react or change as a result of this traumatic event?" |

| Teaching | "Now that we have heard what happened, how you thought about it, the worst part and the signals of distress you have experienced we will give you some information which we believe will help to put things in perspective and help you recover and return to your normal duties and you home life." The CISM team normalizes the experience of the group members and provides practical guidelines to help them recover. |

| Reentry | The main function of the re-entry is to answer any question from the group members and to summarize the discussion and provide any additional guidelines that can assist in their recovery. |

Contraindications:

- Heterogeneous groups and primary victims of a tragedy. **The CISD process should only be used on homogenous groups.**
- Individuals. Do not use a group process on individuals, especially wounded primary victims, such as those who are:
  a. Injured
  b. In severe shock
  c. Ill
  d. In physical pain
  e. Medicated
  f. Showing signs of psychosis
  g. Suicidal
  h. Hospitalized
  i. Bereaved
  j. Extremely fatigued
  k. Under severe emotional distress

l. Brittle, fragile or emotionally distraught
m. Dealing with overwhelming property losses
n. Highly resistant personnel. (Never attempt to force highly resistant personnel to participate in any interactive group crisis intervention process.)

CISD Phases		Objectives
Stage 1	Introduction	To introduce intervention team members, explain process, set expectations.
Stage 2	Fact	To describe traumatic event from each participant's perspective on a cognitive level.
Stage 3	Thought	To allow participants to describe cognitive reactions and to transition to emotional reactions.
Stage 4	Reaction	To identify the most traumatic aspect of the event for the participants and to identify emotional reactions.
Stage 5	Symptom	To identify personal symptoms of distress and transition back to cognitive level.
Stage 6	Teaching	To educate as to normal reactions and adaptive coping mechanisms, i.e., stress management. Provide cognitive anchor.
Stage 7	Re-Entry	To clarify ambiguities, prepare for termination, facilitate "psychological closure," i.e., reconstruction.

KEY CONCEPTS - CISD

- Crisis intervention is not psychotherapy.
- CISD is group crisis intervention, not group psychotherapy or any form of psychotherapy.
- CISD is structured conversation or discussion of a traumatic event
- Goals: 1. Mitigate impact of a crisis/traumatic event
  2. Accelerate normal recovery processes in normal people who are experiencing normal reactions to totally abnormal events
  3. Identify any group member who might need individual support or possibly a referral for professional care.
- Peer support and mental health professionals are used in combination:
  1. **Mental health professional always required**
  2. Peer frequently used in emergency services, hospital based, military, airlines and disaster field workers debriefings
  3. Peer not always required for commercial, business and industrial settings depending on circumstances
  4. CISM trained chaplains are often part of the team.
- **_ALL_** CISM team members must be trained to provide the CISD process regardless of background and other types of training.

- Seven phase process outline: (See alternative prompts above)
  1. **INTRODUCTION**
  2. **FACT**
  3. **THOUGHT**
  4. **REACTION**
  5. **SYMPTOM**
  6. **TEACHING**
  7. **RE-ENTRY**

- One-to-two hours are ideal for a debriefing but the process is dependent on size of the group and may last longer.
- All CISM team members assigned to the CISD are active in the process.
- Avoid probing and psychotherapeutic interpretation.
- Use homogenous groups only.
- Facilitate group discussion.
- Explain the difference between privilege vs. confidential.
- Focus on participants' needs not the CISM team's needs.
- Reaction phase is the most important for processing the event.
- Re-entry phase is the most important for gaining "closure."
- Do not argue with perceptions.
- Provide information and people can change their own perceptions.
- Deal only with material brought out by the participants.
- Avoid detailed operational or investigative information.
- CISD is not a critique of the incident.
- Stick with the model.
- Confidentiality is vital.
- Allow people _not_ to participate in the discussion.
- Do not take notes.
- Provide follow-up. The CISD is not a stand-a-lone process.
- Reserve debriefing for serious events.
- Remember the group is normal, not pathological.
- Keep debriefing conversational and flowing.
- Do not theorize, moralize, psychologically interpret, or judge.
- Team should listen, stabilize, inform, normalize and recover.
- Do not engage in telling "war stories."
- Team members talk actively in the beginning and at the end, less in reaction phase.
- Teach according to the needs of the group and make teaching practical.
- Provide immediate follow up with the most seriously affected personnel.
- Understand the guidelines for referral.
- **Be familiar with and follow guidelines in this manual**

MECHANISM OF ACTION

Both the defusing (see Section 5) and the Critical Incident Stress Debriefing (CISD) interventions appear to derive their effectiveness from several mechanisms of action. That is, the success of the two interactive group processes, Defusing and CISD, depends on the mechanisms of action below, which have a proven track in psychological research:

1) EARLY INTERVENTION. Defusing and the CISD most typically utilize an early intervention strategy, often employed within hours of the traumatic event. Thus, the defusing and, subsequently, the CISD are applied before traumatic memories may be solidified and perhaps distorted and over-generalized.

2) OPPORTUNITY FOR CATHARSIS. Catharsis refers to the release and expression of emotions. The defusing process and the CISD provide a safe, supportive, structured environment wherein individuals can ventilate emotions. In a review of studies specifically investigating the relationship between the disclosure of traumatic events and stress arousal, Pennebaker and Susman (1988) concluded that disclosure of traumatic events leads to reduced stress arousal and improved immune system function.

3) OPPORTUNITY TO VERBALIZE TRAUMA. Defusing and, more so, the CISD not only gives individuals the opportunity to release emotions, but the opportunity to verbally reconstruct and express specific traumas, fears and regrets. van der Hart, Brown and van der Kolk (1989) recount the views of master traumatologist Pierre Janet who noted at the turn of the 20th Century that the successful treatment of post-traumatic reactions was largely based upon the person's ability to reconstruct and integrate the trauma using the verbally expressive medium, as well as expression of feelings (catharsis).

4) STRUCTURE. The CISD and, to a lesser extent, the defusing provides a finite behavioral structure, i.e., a group CISD represents a finite beginning and a finite end, superimposed upon a traumatic event representing chaos, suffering, and a myriad of unanswered questions.

5) GROUP SUPPORT. CISD, in its classic application, employs a group education model. The value of using a group format to address distressing issues is well documented. Yalom (1985, 2005) notes that the group format provides numerous healing factors intrinsic to the group format itself. Among them are the exchange of useful constructive information, catharsis, the dissolution of the myth of a unique weakness among individuals, the modeling of constructive coping behavior, the opportunity to derive a sense of group caring and support, the opportunity to help oneself by helping others and, perhaps most importantly with regard to trauma, the generation of feelings of hope.

6) PEER SUPPORT. The defusing is completely peer driven. Mental health professional are rarely involved in the defusing for emergency personnel. They may be more involved in a defusing for non-emergency personnel. Although mental health professionals oversee the CISD process, it is essentially a peer-driven process. Carkhuff and Truax (1965) demonstrated the value of lay support models. Indeed, peer support interventions offer unique advantages over traditional mental health services, especially when the peer-group views itself as being highly unique, selective, or otherwise _different_ compared to the general population.

7) OPPORTUNITY FOR FOLLOW-UP. Both the defusing and the more thorough CISD process represents an entry portal where potential victims

can engage in group discussion, information exchange, and support. It also represents a mechanism wherein individuals who do require formal psychological care can be identified and helped so as to maximize the likelihood of rapid and total recovery.

Summary

Defusing and Critical Incident Stress Debriefing are interactive group crisis interventions designed by the author of this manual (Mitchell, 1983; 1988a; 1988b; 1991) specifically for the reduction and control of post-traumatic stress reactions among high-intensity and high-risk occupational groups such as fire fighters, emergency medical personnel, law enforcement personnel, public safety, dispatch personnel, the military, disaster workers and other high risk occupations such as transportation industries.

The 40-year period since their origination has revealed significant proliferation and expanding applications worldwide. The efforts of Mitchell and Everly (1993; 1996; 2001) and Mitchell (2007) represent the only major source of operational "how to" guidelines for implementing CISD and defusing interventions. Although there remains a need for additional controlled research, the defusing and CISD processes have been found helpful by many thousands of people in countries around the globe.

References

Adler, A., Litz, B., Castro, C. A., Suvak, M., Thomas, J. L., Burrell, L...
Bliese, P. D. (2008). A group randomized trial of critical incident stress
debriefing provided to U.S. peacekeepers. *Journal of Traumatic Stress,
21*(3), 253-263.

Adler, A., Bliese, P. D, McGurk, D., Hoge, C. W, & Castro, C. A. (2009).
Battlemind debriefing and battlemind training as early interventions
with soldiers returning from Iraq: Randomization by platoon. *Journal
of Consulting and Clinical Psychology, 77,* 928-940.

Amir, M., Weil, G. Kaplan, Z., Tocker, T. and Witzum, E. (1998). Debriefing
with group psychotherapy in a homogenous group of non-injured
victims of a terrorist attack: A prospective study. Acta Psychiatriaca
Scandinavica, *98,* 237-242.

Appel, J. W., Beebe, G. W., & Hilgardner, D. W. (1946). Comparative incidence
of neuropsychiatric casualties in World War I and World War II.
American Journal of Psychiatry, 102, 196-199.

Bohl, N. (1991). The effectiveness of brief psychological interventions in police
officers after critical incidents. In J. T. Reese and J. Horn, and C.
Dunning (Eds.) *Critical Incidents in Policing, Revised* (pp.31-38).
Washington, DC: Department of Justice.

Bohl, N. (1995). Measuring the effectiveness of CISD. *Fire Engineering,* 125-
126.

Boscarino, J. A., Adams, R. E., & Figley, C. R. (2005). A prospective cohort
study of the effectiveness of employer-sponsored crisis interventions
after a major disaster. *International Journal of Emergency Mental
Health, 7,* 9-22.

Boscarino, J. A., Adams, R. E., Foa, E. B., & Landrigan, P. J. (2006). A
propensity score analysis of brief worksite crisis interventions after the
World Trade Center disaster: implications for intervention and
research. *Medical Care*; *44*(5), 454-62.

Boscarino, J. A., & Adams, R. E. (2008). Overview of findings from the World
Trade Center disaster outcome study: Recommendations for future
research after exposure to psychological trauma. *International Journal
of Emergency Mental Health, 10* (4), 275-290.

Boscarino, J. A., Adams, R. E. & Figley, C. R. (2011). Mental health service use after the world trade center disaster: Utilization trends and comparative effectiveness. *Journal of Nervous and Mental Disease, 199,* 91-99.

Breslau, N., Davis, G. C., & Andreski, P. (1991). Traumatic events and post-traumatic stress disorder in an urban population of young adults. *Archives of General Psychiatry, 48,* 216-222.

Breznitz, S. (1980). Stress in Israel. In. H. Selye (Ed.) *Selye's Guide to Stress Research.* (pp.71-89). New York, NY: Van Nostrand Reinhold Co.

Brown, M. W., & Williams, F. E. (1918). *Neuropsychiatry and the war: A bibliography with abstracts.* New York, NY: National Committee for Mental Hygiene.

Campfield, K. & Hills, A. (2001). Effect of timing of critical incident stress debriefing (CISD) on posttraumatic symptoms. *Journal of Traumatic Stress, 14,* 327-340.

Carkhuff, R., & Traux C. (1965). Lay mental health counseling. *Journal of Consulting Psychology, 29,* 426-431.

Castro, C. A., & Adler, A. B. (2011). Re-conceptualizing combat-related posttraumatic stress disorder as an occupational hazard. In A. B. Adler, P. B. Bliese, & C. A. Castro (Eds.), Deployment Psychology: Evidence-Based Strategies to Promote Mental Health in the Military (pp. 217-242). Washington, D.C.: American Psychological Association.

Chemtob, C., Tomas, S., Law, W., & Cremniter, D. (1997). Post disaster psychosocial intervention. *American Journal of Psychiatry, 134,* 415-41

Deahl, M., Srinivasan, M., Jones, N., Thomas, J., Neblett, C., & Jolly, A. (2000). Preventing psychological trauma in soldiers: The role of operational stress training and psychological debriefing. *British Journal of Medical Psychology, 73,* 77-85.

Deahl, M. P., Srinivasan, M., Jones, N., Neblett, C, & Jolly, A. (2001). Evaluating psychological debriefing: Are we measuring the right outcomes? *Journal of Traumatic Stress, 14,* 527-529.

Dyregrov, A. (1998). Psychological debriefing: An effective method? *TRAUMATOLOGYe, 4*(2), Article 1.

Everly, G. (1989). *A clinical guide to the treatment of the human stress response.* New York, NY: Plenum Press.

Hawker, D. M., Durkin, J., & Hawker, D. S. J. (2010). To debrief or not to debrief our heroes: That is the question. *Clinical Psychology and Psychotherapy,* Published online in Wiley Online Library (wileyonlinelibrary.com). doi: 10.1002/cpp.730

Herman, J. L. (1992). Complex PTSD. *Journal of Traumatic Stress, 5,* 377-392.

Jenkins, S. R. (1996). Social support and debriefing efficacy among emergency medical workers after a mass shooting incident. *Journal of Social Behavior and Personality 11,* 447-492

Leonhardt, J. (2006). Critical incident stress management (CISM) in air traffic control (ATC). In J. Leonhardt and J. Vogt (Eds.) *Critical incident stress management CISM in aviation* (pp 81-91). Aldershot, UK: Ashgate Publishing Company.

Mitchell, J. T. (1983). When disaster strikes...The critical incident stress debriefing process. *Journal of Emergency Medical Services, 8,* 36-39.

Mitchell, J. T. (1988a). History, status and future of CISD. *Journal of Emergency Medical Services, 13,* 49-52.

Mitchell, J. T. (1988b). Development and functions of a critical incident stress debriefing team. *Journal of Emergency Medical Services, 13,* 43-46.

Mitchell, J. T. (1991). Law enforcement applications of critical incident stress debriefing teams. In J. T. Reese (Ed.), *Critical Incidents in Policing* (pp. 289-302). Washington, DC: U.S. Department of Justice.

Mitchell, J. T., & Everly, G. S. (2001). *Critical incident stress debriefing: An operations manual for CISD, defusing and other group crisis intervention services* (3rd ed.). Ellicott City, MD: Chevron Publishing.

National de L'urgence Medico-Psychologigue. New York, NY: United Nations, Department of Safety and Security.

Nurmi, L. (1999). The sinking of the Estonia: The effects of critical incident stress debriefing on rescuers. *International Journal of Emergency Mental Health, 1,* 23-32.

Pennebaker, J., & Susman, J. (1988). Disclosure of traumas and psychosomatic processes. *Social Science, and Medicine, 26,* 327-332.

Richards, D. (2001). A field study of critical incident stress debriefing versus critical incident stress management. *Journal of Mental Health, 10,* 351-362.

Regel, S. (2007). Post-trauma support in the workplace: the current status and practice of critical incident stress management (CISM) and psychological debriefing (PD) within organizations in the UK. *Occupational Medicine, 57,* 411-416.

Regel, S. (2010) Does psychological debriefing work? *Healthcare Counselling and Psychotherapy Journal. 10(2), 14-18.*

Robinson, R. and Mitchell, J. (1993). Evaluation of psychological debriefings. *Journal of Traumatic Stress, 6,* 367-382.

Salmon, T. W. (1919). War neuroses and their lesson. *New York Medical Journal, 109,* 993- 994.

Tuckey, M. R. (2007). Issues in the debriefing debate for the emergency services. *Clinical Psychology Science and Practice, 14, 106-16*

Tuckey, M. R., & Scott, J. E. (2013). Group critical incident stress Debriefing with emergency services personnel: A randomized controlled trial. *Anxiety, Stress, and Coping; 27*(1) 38-54.

United Nations Department of Safety and Security CISMU Staff (2007a). UNDSS CISMU certification training for counselors. *DSS Newsletter.* New York, NY: United Nations Secretariat, Department of Safety and Security.

United Nations Department of Safety and Security CISMU Staff (2007b). New crisis and stress management training programme launched. *I Seek (May 2, 2007)* New York, NY: United Nations Secretariat.

United Nations Department of Safety and Security CISMU Staff (2007c). *Certification training in crisis and stress management.* New York: UN Department of Safety and Security, Consultative Working Group on Stress in Collaboration with the International Critical Incident Stress Foundation, the American Academy of Experts in Traumatic Stress and the Comite

Vogt, J., Leonhardt, J., Koper, B. & Pennig, S. (2004). Economic evaluation of CISM – A pilot study. *International Journal of Emergency Mental Health, 6*(4), 185-196.

Vogt, J., Pennig, S. & Leonhardt, J. (2007). Critical incident stress management in air traffic control and its benefits. Air Traffic Control Quarterly, *15*(2), 127-156.

van der Hart, O., Brown, P., & van der Kolk, B. (1989). Pierre Janet's treatment of post-traumatic stress. *Journal of Traumatic Stress, 2,* 379-396.

Wee, D. F., Mills, D. M. & Koelher, G. (1999). The effects of critical incident stress debriefing on emergency medical services personnel following the Los Angeles civil disturbance. *International Journal of Emergency Mental Health, 1,* 33-38.

Western Management Consultants. (1996). *The medical services branch CISM evaluation report.* Edmonton Alberta: WMC.

Wheat, K., & Regel, S. (2003). Early interventions following exposure to traumatic events: Psychological debriefing and the law. *Journal of Personal Injury Law,* Dec 225-236.

Yalom, I. (1985). *Theory and practice of group psychotherapy* (3rd ed.). New York, NY: Basic Books.

Further Readings

Caplan, G. (1961). *An approach to community mental health.* New York, NY: Grune and Stratton.

Caplan, G. (1964). *Principles of preventive psychiatry.* New York, NY: Basic Books.

Eid, J., Johnsen, B. H., & Weisaeth, L. (2001). The effects of group psychological debriefing on acute stress reactions following a traffic accident: a quasi-experimental approach. *International Journal of Emergency Mental Health, 3,* 145-154.

Everly, G.S., Jr. (2013). Fostering human resilience. Ellicott City, MD: Chevron Publishing.

Everly, G. S. and Mitchell, J. T. (2013) *critical incident stress management CISM: Key papers and core concepts.* Ellicott City, MD: Chevron Publishing.

Gibson, M. (2006). *Order from chaos: Responding to traumatic events.* Bristol, UK : The Policy Press

Hassling, P. (2000). Disaster management and the Gothenburg fire of 1998: when first responders are blamed. *International Journal of Emergency Mental Health, 2*(2) 267-273.

Kobassa, S. C. (1979). Stressful life events, personality, and health: An inquiry into hardiness. *Journal of Personality and Social Psychology, 37,* 1-11.

Kobassa, S. C., Maddi, S. R., & Kahn, S. (1982). Hardiness and health: a prospective study. *Journal of Personality and Social Psychology, 42,* 168-177.

Lazarus, R. S. (1966). *Psychological stress and the coping process.* New York, NY: McGraw-Hill

Lazarus, R. S. (1969). *Patterns of adjustment and human effectiveness.* New York, NY: McGraw-Hill.

Lifton, R. J. (1970). *History and human survival: Essays on the young and the old, survivors and the dead, peace and war, and on contemporary psychohistory.* New York, NY: Random House.

Lifton, R. J. (1973). *Home from the war: Vietnam veterans—neither victims nor executioners.* New York, NY: Simon & Schuster.

Lifton R. J. (1993). *The protean self: Human resilience in an age of fragmentation,* New York, NY: Basic Books.

Mitchell, J. T. (2007). *Group crisis support: Why it works, when and how to provide it.* Ellicott City, MD: Chevron Publishing.

Myers, D. and Wee, D. (2005). *Disaster mental health services: A primer for Practitioners.* New York, NY: Brunner-Routledge.

Roberts, A. (2005). Bridging the past and present to the future of crisis intervention and crisis management. In Allen Roberts (Ed.) *Crisis Intervention Handbook: Assessment, Treatment and Research. Third Edition.* New York, NY: Oxford University Press.

Vogt, J. & Leonhardt, J. (Eds.). (2006). *Critical incident stress management in aviation.* Hampshire, UK: Ashgate Publishing Limited.

Section Eight

CISD Practice Session

Something to think about:

Knowledge is of no value unless you put it into practice.
Anton Chekhov

Complete training in the Critical Incident Stress Debriefing (CISD) requires practical experience. One way to achieve that Practical experience is for the training group to participate in or observe a CISD demonstration or role-play.

The course instructor will present a scenario to a group of role players selected from the attendees at the training. The instructor usually leads the CISD demonstration. Some attendees will play the peer support roles. Others will play out roles as members of a homogeneous group that has been exposed to the traumatic event. Some from among the attendees will be selected to be observers of the CISD role-play.

On the following pages is a form that observers may use to keep up with the CISD process or to develop question for the discussion following the CISD.

Observing a CISD Exercise

1. The CISD has 7 separate stages. Write down what happened during the CISD, which you observed, that indicated the beginning of each of the stages listed below:

    a. Introduction-

    b. Fact – (brief situation review)

    c. Thought – (first impression)

    d. Reaction – (aspects causing greatest personal impact)

    e. Symptom – (signals of distress)

    f. Teaching – (stress management and recovery guidelines)

    g. Re-entry – (summary)

2. Who was in control of the CISD? What things were done which indicated control?

    Verbal -

    Non-verbal -

3. The CISD not only progresses through each of the 7 functional phases, it also progresses psychologically from the Cognitive (thought) Domain to the Affective (emotional) Domain and back to the Cognitive Domain. Indicate what happened to initiate the beginning of each of these domains:

   Cognitive Domain -

   Affective Domain -

   Cognitive Domain —

4. Did the debriefing achieve a sense of psychological closure to the critical incident described? If so, how? If not, why not?

5. If you were the team leader for the debriefing you just observed, what would you plan to do at the end of the debriefing?

Appendix I

Personal and Community Resilience

Something to think about:

"When we tackle obstacles, we find hidden reserves of courage and resilience we did not know we had. And it is only when we are faced with failure do we realise that these resources were always there within us. We only need to find them and move on with our lives."
A. P. J. Abdul Kalam (Aerospace engineer and former president of India)

** IMPORTANT INFORMATION **

The Resiliency Model In Crisis Work and Stress Management

BACKGROUND

From the very beginning, Critical Incident Stress Management (CISM) was, and continues to be, a crisis system based on a resiliency model. It aims at building resistance before exposure to traumatic events. It focuses on rebounding from stress. In those cases where people need additional care, the CISM program is uniquely positioned to assist individuals in finding appropriate professional care to help them recover from traumatic experience.

APPLICATION ESSENTIALS

Resistance - *Resistance is the ability of individuals, groups, organizations, and entire populations to resist distress, impairment, and dysfunction.* One way to look at resistance is to think about it as if it were a certain degree of immunity. If we make ourselves resistant enough, we can ward off many of the harmful effects of traumatic incidents. *Resistance is the foundation of resilience.* Resistance can be developed. Training, education, healthy living, exercise, and enhanced life style behaviors and attitudes long before the traumatic event strikes are the best methods to develop resistance. If you build resistance you also enhance resilience. Resistance (and thus resilience) is built up by preparation for stressful experiences and the practice of stress management skills. In summary, resistance is the build-up of protective factors to make us stress-resistant. Protective factors include self-esteem, optimism, improved nutrition, appropriate sleep habits, social support, family life, exercise, avoidance of non-prescription drugs and tobacco, and limitation of alcohol use.

Resilience - *The ability to rapidly rebound or recoil from distress, and to rise above adversity.* Every person is born with some resilience, but the work done in building resistance improves our ability to be resilient over time and when faced with adversity.

Warning signs that your resilience is low and needs a recharge.

- Boredom
- Fatigue
- Anxiety
- Depression
- Anger / Irritability
- Withdrawal

METHODS TO MAINTAIN AND ENHANCE RESILIENCE

1. Calming, Optimism, and Happiness

- Calm the heart and mind and the brain will calm as well.
- Use deep breathing. Breathe in a deep breath through your nose; hold your breath 8 seconds; breathe out all the air through pursed lips. Repeat three times, but rest in between each deep breath.
- Try tensing and relaxing muscle groups. Work from the feet toward the head. Tense a muscle group; hold tight 5 to 8 seconds; release tension.
- Substitute positive thoughts for negative ones. "I can handle this" instead of "I am doomed."
- Maintain optimism even with the odds against you. Try to find something that is positive or an advantage.

- Choose happiness.
- Spend more time with happy people; avoid the chronically unhappy people.
- Smile more.
- Compliment others.
- Be a friend to others.

2. Manage Stress to Build Resilience

- Exercise regularly a minimum of 3 times a week and about 20 minutes at a time
- Sleep about 7 hours a night
- Brief power naps during the day can help
- Add movement to your work time. Do not sit still all the time
- Have adequate sunlight
- Eat brain healthy nutrition (vegetables, fruits, nuts, whole grain breads, proteins, etc.)
- Reduce sugar in your diet; reduce carbohydrates
- Avoid alcohol
- Avoid non-prescription drugs
- Avoid all products containing nicotine

3. Prepare for Crisis

- Train, practice for emergencies, build skills
- Learn to assess, analyze, adapt, and alter plans as necessary
- Understand that emotions will change and be intense during a crisis
- Know that normal relationships with others can be altered while under duress. Most are restored with time.
- Be open to individual and group support after crisis. They help to maintain healthy individuals and work teams.

4. Take Action

- Try something
- Be flexible
- Assess, analyze, problem solve, decide, and take action

- Indecision and inaction are highly stressful
- Be prepared to take moderate risks
- Manage distressing emotions
- Alter the course of action if failure is imminent

5. Social Support

- Have a life outside of the job
- Develop friendships
- Respect those who earned it
- Work to gain the respect of others
- Be friendly to all
- Give public praise, but private criticisms
- Don't talk behind someone's back
- Know that Gossip kills friendship
- Choose positive, motivated people to be with

6. Self-Esteem

- Self-esteem is the midpoint between pride and shame
- All people are worth something
- Mistakes do not mean that you have no value. They just mean you are human
- Resilient people believe they can be a change agent in the lives of others

7. **Recovery** – *The resolution, repair, reconstruction, restoration, and rebuilding of the human spirit, mind, and body after sustaining the damages incurred by prolonged, extreme, or overwhelming distress.*

- Recovery is about regaining control
- Recovery re-establishes resilience
- Recovery means we come to terms with the experiences that hurt us, shocked us and drained our resilience
- Recovery is reigniting the spark that lights the flame that makes life worth living
- Be prepared to seek help. Recovery is very difficult without a support system.

- Recovery frequently takes the support and guidance of professionals
- Family, Friends and Colleagues should also take a role in a person's recovery
- Recovery is part of resilience.
- Recovery means you have the resilience and the courage to reignite the spark.

Beyond recovery are the lessons we can learn from life's horrible experiences. We should learn that we could recover, even in what we consider the worst cases. All is not lost simply because we were damaged by tragedy. Occasionally, good things come out of tragic events. Recovery does not mean that we are without painful memories or psychological scars. Recovery means that we are willing to move ahead, to grow, and to find meaning in life despite those memories, wounds, and scars.

Colonel Richard Jaehne, USMC (Retired) gives us some guiding principles on recovery (what he calls "coming back"). Colonel Jaehne was seriously wounded in Viet Nam. He developed Posttraumatic Stress Disorder (PTSD). He refused, however, to let the enemy or PTSD take over his life. He achieved his military mission in battle and overcame the enemy. He was resilient in dealing with PTSD and he restored his resilience. He recovered. He remained an active member of the United States Marine Corp until his retirement. Toward the end of his career, he was entrusted with command of global Marine Corp operations. To "come back" (to recover) he says you need five essential ingredients:

1. You have to have something to come back to.
2. You must be acknowledged in some way for the contributions you made.
3. You have to find ways to give something back.
4. You have to have a belief in a power beyond yourself.
5. You have to have courage.

144

Appendix II

CISM Terms Used by the United Nations and Non-Governmental Organizations (NGO) Working with the United Nations

In 2007, three Critical Incident Stress Management (CISM) terms were altered in response to a request from the United Nations for a change in certain terms that were difficult to translate into a number of languages. The terms were "demobilization," "defusing," and "Critical Incident Stress Debriefing." Around the same time, military forces in several countries were requesting that CISM drop the use of the term "demobilization" since it was widely used by military forces and CISM's use of the term was causing confusion.

The word "demobilization" has been completely dropped in the CISM field. A description of the process was substituted for the word demobilization. The appropriate term now is "Rest, Information, Transition Services" (RITS). Section 4 of this manual reflects that change. No change has been made to the process. Everything else about demobilization is the same as it has always been.

One caution. Always use the full term, "Rest, Information, and Transition Services" or RITS. The fire service uses a similar term "RIT" for Rapid Intervention Team. The terms and purposes of the intervention are quite different.

NOTE: The demobilization process itself has not changed. Only the title of the intervention has been changed to accommodate the United Nations and military forces.

The following terms have been changed for United Nations purposes. _Only_ the United Nations and NGO's working with the United Nations are using these terms. The remainder of the CISM field continues to use the traditional CISM terminology.

A. "Defusing" (for UN purposes only). This term has been altered to "Immediate Small Group Support" (ISGS).

B. "Critical Incident Stress Debriefing" (CISD). For UN purposes only, this term has been altered to "Powerful Event Group Support (PEGS)."

Only the names have been changed to suit the UN needs. The content and the applications of the processes did not change at all. *"Defusing" and "Critical Incident Stress Debriefing (CISD)" remain the preferred terms for everyone outside of the UN.*

Please _DO NOT USE_ these terms:
1) "Immediate Small Group Support" or
2) "Powerful Event Group Support," unless you are working directly under UN control or as an NGO with the United Nations.

Appendix III

CIS

INFORMATION

SHEETS

The following pages may be reproduced with full permission of the International Critical Incident Stress Foundation, Inc.

CRITICAL INCIDENT STRESS INFORMATION SHEETS ©

You have experienced a traumatic event or a critical incident (any event that causes unusually strong emotional reactions that have the potential to interfere with the ability to function normally). Even though the event may be over, you may now be experiencing or may experience later, some strong emotional or physical reactions. It is very common, in fact quite *normal*, for people to experience emotional aftershocks when they have passed through a horrific event.

Sometimes the emotional aftershocks (or stress reactions) appear immediately after the traumatic even. Or they may appear a few hours or a few days later. And, in some cases, weeks or months may pass before the stress reactions appear.

The signs of symptoms of a stress reaction may last a few days, a few weeks, a few months, or longer, depending on the severity of the traumatic event. The understanding and the support of loved ones usually cause the stress reactions to pass more quickly. Occasionally, the traumatic event is so painful that professional assistance may be necessary. This does not imply mental instability or weakness. It simply indicates that the particular event was just too powerful for the person to manage by himself.

Here are some common signs and signals of a stress reaction:

Physical*	Cognitive	Emotional	Behavioral
chills	confusion	fear	withdrawal
thirst	nightmares	guilt	antisocial acts
fatigue	uncertainty	grief	inability to rest
nausea	hypervigilance	panic	intensified pacing
fainting	suspiciousness	denial	erratic movements
twitches	intrusive images	anxiety	change in social activity
vomiting	blaming someone	agitation	change in speech patterns
dizziness	poor problem solving	irritability	change in appetite
weakness	poor abstract thinking	depression	hyperalert to environment
chest pain	poor attention/decisions	intense anger	increased alcohol consumption
headaches	poor concentration/ memory	apprehension	change in usual communications
elevated BP	disorientation of time, place or person	emotional outbursts	
rapid heart rate	difficulty identifying objects or people	loss of emotional control	
muscle tremors	heightened or lowered alertness	inappropriate emotional response	
shock symptoms	increased or decreased awareness of surroundings	emotional shock	
grinding of teeth		feeling overwhelmed	
visual difficulties			
profuse sweating			
difficulty breathing			

*Any of these symptoms may indicate the need for medical evaluation. When in doubt, contact a physician.

THINGS TO TRY

- WITHIN THE FIRST 24 – 48 HOURS: periods of appropriate physical exercise, alternated with relaxation will alleviate some of the physical reactions.
- Structure your time; keep busy
- You're normal and having normal reactions; don't label yourself crazy.
- Talk to people; talk is the most healing medicine
- Be aware of *numbing* the pain with overuse of drugs or alcohol. You don't need to complicate this with a substance abuse problem.
- Reach out; people do care.
- Maintain as normal a schedule as possible
- Spend time with others
- Help your co-workers as much as possible by sharing feelings and checking out how they are doing.
- Give yourself permission to feel rotten and share your feelings with others.
- Keep a journal; write your way through those sleepless hours.
- Do things that feel good to you.
- Realize those around you are under stress
- Don't make any big life changes.
- Do make as many daily decisions as possible that will give you a feeling of control over your life; i.e., if someone asks you what you want to eat, answer them even if you're not sure.
- Get plenty of rest.
- Don't try to fight reoccurring thoughts, dreams, or flashbacks – they are normal and will decrease over time and become less painful.
- Eat well-balanced and regular meals (even if you don't feel like it).

FOR FAMILY MEMBERS AND FRIENDS

- Listen carefully
- Spend time with traumatized person
- Offer your assistance and a listening ear if they have not asked for help
- Reassure them that they are safe
- Help them with everyday tasks like cleaning, cooking, caring for the family, minding children
- Give them some private time
- Don't take their anger or other feelings personally
- Don't tell them that they are 'lucky it wasn't worse;' a traumatized person is not consoled by such statements. Instead, tell them that you are sorry such an event has occurred and you want to understand and assist them.